WEIGHT TRAINING

for

HOCKEY

THE ULTIMATE GUIDE

This book aims to teach hockey players how to better manage their weight training program. The application of the information provided in this book does not guarantee any results. The materials contained in this book are provided for general information purposes only and do not constitute professional advice on any subject matter. This book does not, in any way, replace the advice of a qualified medical practitioner, health practitioner, or fitness professional. You must always seek the advice of a trained healthcare professional or a physician with any questions you may have regarding your own specific condition before beginning any program of weight lifting, exercise or diet provided in this book. Please note that all matters regarding your health require supervision. In addition, during the specific physical assessments suggested in this book, you must be assisted by another person to avoid any kind of injury, loss or damage. Neither your acquisition nor your use of this book establishes any doctor-patient relationship, or any therapeutic relationship, between you and the author. Moreover, neither the author nor any person associated with this book will be liable or responsible for any injury, loss, or damage sustained by any person acting directly or indirectly, in part or in whole, on the basis of any information contained in this book. Finally, application of the techniques, ideas, and suggestions presented in this book is done at the reader's sole discretion and risk.

Price World Publishing
3971 Hoover Rd. Suite 77
Columbus, OH 43123-2839
www.PriceWorldPublishing.com

Cover Design by Russell Marleau
Layout Design by Merwin Loquias
Editing by Vanessa Fravel
Printing by United Graphics

ISBN: 978-1-932549-829
eBook ISBN: 978-1-619843-493
Library of Congress Control Number: 2013931809

Printed in the United States of America
10 9 8 7 6 5 4 3 2 1
For information about discounts for bulk purchases, please contact info@priceworldpublishing.com.

WEIGHT TRAINING

for

HOCKEY

THE ULTIMATE GUIDE

DR. DENIS BOUCHER, PH.D.

PRICE WORLD
PUBLISHING

TABLE OF CONTENTS

ACKNOWLEDGEMENTS

All data related to on-ice testing are presented with the authorization of M2M Lab Inc.

We want to thank Physiotec.ca for allowing us to create the training programs using their Health and Fitness Exercise Software.

We also want to thank Allan Ross from Ross and Sheehan for his help in revising this text.

INTRODUCTION

In 1999, my business partner at that time and I invested in a new company, and we were among the first in Canada to buy what was known as a portable respiratory gas analyzer. This system would allow us to evaluate the fitness level (VO_{2max}) of athletes on the field.

A few weeks later, we received a call from the strength and conditioning coach of the Philadelphia Flyers asking if we could test the VO_{2max} of the players **on the ice**. We said YES!!!!!!!!!!!!

We then evaluated a shuttle test protocol on the ice and, a few weeks later there we were, on the ice with the Flyers.

Even though I already knew that hockey was the most physiologically complex sport of all, it still amazes to this day how complex a sport it really is.

I will present my sport scientist's view of hockey and how you should train. Some of you will surely disagree, but the years of testing and the progress of exercise science points to one important fact: we must make sure that the training hockey players go through brings specific results. As you'll find out, many training result claims are not always backed by objective scientific data. I'm not saying that what I'll present in this book is THE only way to do things. I simply just want you to ask the right question:

- Do you train strategically?

So let's find out if you train strategically. To be 100 percent sure you train strategically, you must be able to answer the following questions:

- – What is your performance goal?
- – What fitness level should you strive for in order to reach your goal?

These are simple questions, but they're not easy to answer. Your training program must help you increase your performance level. However, for too many athletes, performance is an "idea" they have made up in their mind, and I must tell you that defining this idea or concept in a tangible way is a task that may prove to be very difficult. To clarify this vague idea of what performance is, you need to define criteria on the basis of which performance can be clearly measured and evaluated. Once you're able to accomplish this, you can then put together a strategic training plan.

So, this book is not only about weight training. It's about how we can define performance on the ice, how you can evaluate your fitness level, how to determine the gap between where you stand and where you should be to reach you performance goal, and how to train strategically in order to close this gap.

CHAPTER 1
TRAINING STRATEGICALLY

Why is it so important to find out if you train strategically? Because my field and lab experience has shown me that many athletes spend too many hours training at high intensity, yet their fitness level is low considering the amount of training they put in.

How to train strategically

If you want to train strategically, meaning spending the least amount of time training and producing the best possible results, as I indicated above, you need to be able to answer the following questions:

- What is your performance goal?
- What fitness level should you strive for in order to reach your goal?

Two simple questions, but try to answer them right away. It's not that easy. Until you're able to give a clear answer, you won't be able to train strategically and you'll waste all that time training for no clear purpose.

Let me help you out with some sample answers to these questions:

What is your performance goal?
- To increase my speed and resistance on the ice (a realistic and manageable goal).

What fitness level should you strive for in order to reach your goal?
- My max power on the ice is 250 watts. I need to improve my power by 30 watts to reach my goal.
- My VO2max is 46 (on the ice) and I need to increase it to 50.
- My biomechanic efficiency is low and I need to improve my skating technique.

How did you come up with this clear, concise and precious information? You went through a series of fitness tests (which I'll discuss later).

With a realistic and manageable goal, you were then able to pinpoint the gap between your current performance level and the one you need to reach.

Without this knowledge, how can you define the proper training you need to improve your performance?

Reaching a goal

Reaching a performance goal means using strategies that will allow you to close the gap between where you currently stand and the level you need to reach.

Thus, you need to evaluate two variables: what you need to improve and how much you need to improve it.

In order to properly evaluate the gap between your current performance and the performance level you're seeking, you need to take the following steps:

1. Identify the demands and requirements of a given task and evaluate what is needed to bridge the gap between your current and desired abilities.

2. Evaluate the resources that you have and those at your disposal to meet those needs, and assess whether they are adequate and sufficient to allow you to progress and fill this gap, and whether you consider this to be a challenge or a threat. If you consider it to be a threat, this will seriously hinder your progress, even if the deficiencies of these resources are minor. You should therefore take serious initial steps to resolve any shortfall and ensure that, in the back of your mind, you have no doubt whatsoever about the adequacy of the resources at your disposal.

3. Evaluate your feelings about the situation. Athletes who consider the gap to be too wide normally adopt two different techniques that are in both effectively counter-productive: They either deny that such a gap even exists, or they try to manage and perhaps suppress their feelings. In both cases, athletes are using up energy to either forget or control their emotions. Do not use these strategies, as they drain you of your energy and seriously distract you from reaching the desired level of performance, which in turn leads to more errors.

4. Aim for a performance objective which fills the performance gap, and generate a procedure where actions and strategies are put in place to reduce this gap and let you reach your performance goal. The problem is that most athletes, trainers and sport professionals do not critically analyze the strategies they put in place, which results in both ineffective and inefficient planning that does not yield the desired results. You should therefore ask yourself the following questions when implementing your strategy:

> Is the training program effective? Has it been fully adapted to your own needs? If so, how do you actually measure its effectiveness? Are you using concrete and accurate scientific methods to measure this effectiveness?

> As I indicated above, an athlete's performance must be expressed in measurable and quantifiable terms. For example, if you want to be stronger, you need to define how strong and in relation to what. If you need to skate faster, for example, what does skating faster specifically mean for you? What are the muscular and physical qualities that you need to possess to skate faster?

If you ignore these requirements, you will probably end up dropping your training after trying too hard and pushing yourself to exhaustion, without achieving the desired results. You become discouraged by these failed attempts to improve your performance and your motivation suffers.

As I so often see, many of the hockey players I test who want to skate faster assume that they need to increase their leg muscle mass. But when I analyze their test results, muscle mass is not really the issue. In most cases, a lack of power and proper skating technique are the problem. Increasing muscle mass can be helpful to some extent, but it won't necessarily help you skate faster. Furthermore, increasing your speed is one thing, but if you can sustain your maximum speed for only 5 seconds, after which your speed decreases by 50 percent from second 5 to 10, you're not much further ahead. Again, the *contractile quality* of the leg muscles is the real problem, not muscle mass.

Therefore, adopting the best approach requires an accurate definition of performance using quantifiable and measurable criteria, and you have to be very precise. You need to define the physical fitness level you need to reach. To do so, you need to analyze the fitness level of your competitors and assess the difference between yours and theirs to determine the level you need to achieve to rank among the best of the best. I will explain what to do to help you determine where you rank.

By using these precise and specific criteria, you may realize that to be among the best, you do not need to be 20, 30 or 50 percent better than other hockey players, but perhaps only 2 percent better, so your goals become quantifiable, measurable and, most importantly, realistic and achievable. So while you're training, since you understand and know exactly what you need to do to achieve your goals and *perceive* them as achievable, your actions will accurately be carried out in accordance with the criteria you have defined.

Your training strategies have now turned into a very precise plan that will effectively enable you to achieve the desired performance.

You also need to prioritize each of the physical actions you're planning to carry out, each of the training movements that you need to undertake and for each type of exercise that you're going to use. If, for example, you were to prioritize increasing your physical fitness level, you need to allocate more time to this criterion than to the others. Since you only have a certain amount of energy to allocate, you need to do so strategically and acccording to the priority given to each criterion. In other words, by defining measurable and quantifiable criteria, you can precisely allocate your time, energy and resources on the basis of these criteria.

A poor evaluation of your situation will inevitably lead to bad training strategies, with poor results, loss of confidence and motivation and, ultimately, failure. You will never be on the right track. An accurate and precise measurement, on the other hand, gives us an accurate evaluation of your situation and paves the way to achieving desirable results.

Hockey, the most physiologically complex sport

Much of the knowledge that has been gathered in exercise science comes from the study of runners and cyclists in a lab. Under these conditions, it is a simple matter to observe the impact of a progressively increasing workload (exercise intensity) on the physiology of the athletes being tested. Running and cycling are mainly aerobic activities. We know a lot about how to study and evaluate the aerobic capacity of an athlete. We also know a lot of the physiological changes that the body goes through during these types of activities.

However, we know very little about what happens physiologically in sports where bursts of intense exercise (under five minutes) are characteristic features (sprint running and hockey, for example)[1]. Furthermore, skating at high intensity quickly depletes the bioenergetic reserves of the muscle cells. During a game, hockey players execute many bursts of high intensity effort (ranging from a few seconds to at most a few minutes). How these reserves are depleted and replenished throughout a game remains a complex phenomenon to analyze and understand.

Hockey is not a unidimensional sport where you simply need to increase your aerobic and muscular capacity to improve your performance level. To improve your skills, you need to manage many interconnected variables. Hockey players need power, a strong aerobic capacity and amazing anaerobic reserves. This combination of qualities is quite difficult to achieve.

Before we look at these qualities, I invite you to take a crash course in exercise physiology.

Dr. Denis Boucher, Ph.D.

CHAPTER 2
WHAT DO YOU NEED TO KNOW TO BECOME A PHYSICALLY FIT HOCKEY PLAYER

Exercise physiology–a crash course

In exercise physiology, when we talk about oxygen uptake kinetics,[2] we look at the evolution of the oxygen uptake while intensity rises. Your maximal oxygen uptake is called VO_{2max}. Start skating at a slow pace. Then, progressively increase your speed until you reach the maximal effort you can give (I know this is not how it goes in a game, but bear with me). From the moment you start skating until the moment you stop, you will go though many physiological changes. At a slow pace, you find yourself in the aerobic zone, where your muscle cells use lipids to produce the necessary energy for your muscles to contract. In this zone, you could skate for hours. As intensity increases, you reach a point call the anaerobic threshold (AT). The AT is the power at which you begin to produce blood lactate. Above the AT and below the maximal lactate steady state (MLSS), the body reuses blood lactate to produce energy. So, when a player skates at a power level between these two margins (AT- MLSS), the player can skate for a few minutes. The MLSS is the point at which the body starts building up blood lactate, so keeping the pace above this threshold will inevitably lead to exhaustion. The closer a player skates to his maximal power (MAX), the faster exhaustion will occur[3]. In a game, players spend much of their skating time above the MLSS.

For a decade (from 1999 to 2009) the best way to evaluate a player's fitness level was on the ice (shuttle test) using a respiratory gas analyser to evaluate the fitness level of the players. This would give us the two data points we believed were the most important: the anaerobic threshold and the VO_{2max}. It then became quite obvious that we only had a partial picture of the variables that were responsible for the players' performance. Furthurmore, it also became increasingly evident that the anaerobic threshold and the VO_{2max} were only a snapshot of one physiological performance and not a measure nor an explanation of the performance delivered on the ice (how and at what speed the body moves on the ice).

As the technology evolved, a most useful type of device was introduced on the market: biosensors. In two articles published in the The Hockey News magazine entitled: The *Development of On-Ice Testing*[4] and *On-Ice Testing with the Philadelphia Flyers,*[5] I describe how my current associate and I integrated biosensors and used a new protocol to test the players on the ice. This brings us back to the variables that influence performance.

What do you need to be a physically fit hockey player?

In order to gain speed on the ice, you need to be able to translate power into speed and maintain it for many long seconds if necessary. As mentioned above, to accomplish this, you need great muscle power and amazing aerobic and anaerobic capacities.

From the new technology we integrated and the protocol used, we obtained the following information on the skating capacity of the players:

- Power (rated in watts) that the player generated on the ice throughout the test.
- Maximal power generated.
- Power generated by each leg.
- Speed profile throughout the test.
- Length of time the player could sustain his maximal power.
- Critical Power (also known as the maximal lactate steady state).
- Biomechanic efficiency of the skating technique.
- Body posture (upper body inclination).
- Lateral, vertical and sagittal body movements.
- Breathing rate and breathing amplitude (for oxygen delivery efficiency measurement)
- Depletion of bioenergetic reserves

Here are some of our findings:

- The breathing pattern matters. At high intensity, when pain increases, some players engage in a disrupted breathing pattern without even noticing it. Breathing amplitude decreases, while the breathing rate increases, to compensate for the reduced capacity of the respiratory muscles to inflate the torso and bring oxygen to the muscles. Since the breathing rate compensation is not enough, exhaustion occurs faster. In this situation, train the player to breathe effectively and you increase his fitness level immediately.

- If a player has not fully recovered from a lower extremity injury, the injured leg obviously generates less power than the other. At some point, the injured leg can't keep up with the increasing demands of the test, and the maximal capacity occurs before we would normally expect. Train that leg in order to recover the proper balance of power generated by each leg, and you get your player back at full speed.

- A player can generate amazing instant power, but only for a few seconds. Test results reveal that the anaerobic reserves are low. With proper training and nutritional strategies, you can increase the anaerobic reserves quickly, and thus help your player sustain high levels of power for longer periods of time.

- When fatigue and pain increase, the player adopts an almost upright position, rather than keeping the upper body inclined. As a result, his biomechanic efficiency drops, fatigue and pain increase exponentially and exhaustion occurs quickly. Correct this problem and you increase the player's efficiency in no time.

As you can see, it's all about what makes muscle mass efficient and not just about muscle mass per se.

To be a good skater you need to translate power into speed and, as you're doing this, if you can't control even one variable like breathing or body posture … you're done.

Being in excellent physical shape is a prerequisite to performance but, sadly, it doesn't guarantee good results unless you master the variables I've just introduced.

The aerobic capacity of hockey players and the levels they should reach

I cannot overstate the fact that hockey has nothing to do with cycling or running. We all know that good aerobic capacity is important, but to what extent is this true for hockey players? Excellent runners will have a VO_{2max} above 70, excellent cyclists score above 75 and excellent cross-country skiers score above 80. For a hockey player, I consider that a VO_{2max} (tested on the ice) of 53 to 55 is good, from 56 to 59 is excellent and above 60 is awesome. But why is it so different from other sports? The answer lies in how the muscle mass of the legs is used.

Because hockey players must produce and sustain a high level of muscle contraction, a high aerobic capacity will never compensate for a lack of muscle strength. You must invest your training time to improve both your aerobic capacity and muscle strength (I'll discuss muscle power later).

With this in mind, you can manage your training more strategically and invest your training time to improve the right qualities. You'll eventually reach a point where you'll simply have to maintain your current aerobic capacity and muscle strength.

Remember, the goal is to train less with better results.

Biomechanic efficiency

Skating involves complex movements. The player must propel himself forward efficiently. But, even with an excellent aerobic capacity and great muscle power, which are basic qualities of a good athlete, you won't skate fast or effectively without good skating technique. Remember, you must translate power into speed, and if your skating technique produces more resistance on the ice than it should, the power you generate will be lost and you won't gain any speed.

In my opinion, many hockey players overestimate their skating skills and should invest more time on that aspect of their training. The results I'll present below will give you a good idea of what I'm talking about.

High speed and recovery alternance

You've trained hard. You've gained in aerobic fitness and power. On the ice, however, you skate fast, then slow down, and seconds later you produce another high intensity outburst. You alternate between high intensity effort and different levels of recovery.

You will always be confronted with your limits. No matter how fit you are, you have to manage your energy. This is why it's important to test yourself to get to know your muscular and physiological performance profile. Knowing how long you can sustain a given speed and how fast you can recover is of great importance.

Another important aspect of your training program is muscle fatigue management.

Muscular fatigue (sustainable and non-sustainable intensities)

Winning involves the notion of pushing past your limits. But, as mentioned above, your physical resources are limited. Muscle fatigue is the other dimension of athletic success. Obviously, the level of physical fitness affects fatigue, but several other fairly complex mechanisms also factor into the equation.

As a hockey player, you will inevitably reach your maximum capacity. At that point, you can no longer continue to maintain the same level of effort, and this is what defines muscle fatigue. It is important to realize, however, that fatigue always appears as a result of a specific task or performance. Thus, there are several types of muscle fatigue, each of which can present its own set of specific characteristics. In short, with an understanding of the specific context in which athletes deploy physical effort, the determining factors of fatigue can be more accurately identified so they can in turn be "manipulated".

Fatigue takes over the body and no human can sustain a given effort indefinitely. In order to decipher the fatigue process, science has been exploring various avenues to try to understand its origins. The central nervous system, reduction in glycogen reserves, reduction in muscle energy reserves and reduction in ATP (adenosine-triphosphate) reserves are among the systems under study. It should be explained at this point that energy substrates, (carbohydrates, lipids and proteins) are used in ATP synthesis. ATP provides the chemical energy required for muscle contraction. Although energy substrate levels diminish under effort, ATP synthesis remains constant. Energy production is therefore not diminished. Once again, the reduction in energy reserves does not provide us with a complete explanation. And what about blood lactate? Long considered as metabolic waste, it is actually a source of energy, because it is used by muscles and other organs such as the heart to produce energy. Muscle cells tire under effort. What is often overlooked, however, is that at the same time, other cells are recovering. Here again, we are struck by an oddity of nature: muscle fatigue and muscle recovery occur simultaneously under full effort.

In my laboratory, we also look at several perceptual, sensory and cognitive factors related to athletic performance. We thus manipulate several variables that affect human and motor behaviour: fear, stress, anticipation, expectations, sensory perceptions, perception of time and perceived pain. In terms of endurance, our observations indicate that in doing so, we do not directly improve an athlete's physical fitness (VO_{2max}). We do, however, manage to delay the onset of fatigue, or alter its significance for the athletes, which considerably increases their performance.

Fear, worry, stress, anticipation, negative emotions and interpretation of sensory information have a significant impact on the physiological and biomechanical reactions of athletes. Thus, as the brains of athletes are "hijacked" by information they perceive as threatening, they will experience fatigue prematurely.

Let's play some more with your perceptions. I take you into my laboratory and place weights in a crate and ask you to lift it. We repeat this exercise until you have reached your maximum lifting capacity. Let's say you can lift no more than 120 lbs. One of my assistants a little farther away places a 120-lb weight in another crate of the same size and colour. I ask you to give me a hand to move this crate that contains the same load that you just lifted, because my assistant is not strong enough to lift it by himself. You go over to the crate, pick it up, and place it where my assistant asks you to. But before completing this additional task, I omitted to tell you that the crate itself weighs 15 lbs. You therefore lifted 135 lbs rather than the 120 lbs that you had just identified as your maximum physical lifting capacity. Indeed, what your mind thinks, or what it doesn't know, affects your muscle capacity.

Most athletes spend enormous amounts of time planning their training, nutrition and recovery period, which is obviously essential. Rarely, however, do we meet athletes who plan their thoughts and their physiological reactions to enable their bodies to react with maximum efficiency.

I thus seek to define fatigue on the basis of the task to be performed. As a result, the type of fatigue felt, its onset, duration and intensity become variables that can be manipulated to enable athletes to take full control of them.

By looking at muscle fatigue as a resource that can be managed and manipulated, rather than a detrimental consequence, surprising possibilities can suddenly become within our reach.

Don't worry, I'll summarize of all this information in order to help you better manage your training program.

Muscle contraction

What allows you to skate or shoot the puck is muscle contraction. When the intensity is low, you recruit a small volume of muscle mass, but as intensity increases, you need to recruit more muscle mass. Simple logic, but physiologically it's a different game.

In a recent article, authors Matthew W. Bundle and Peter G. Weyand[1] have reported some important points that we also observed following on-ice tests done with professional hockey players. Here are some of the important facts that I want to underscore:

"… the greatest decrements in performance occur across those efforts that span the briefest durations. For example, the decrements that occur as effort durations extend from 2 to 30 s are much larger than those that occur with duration increases from 30 to 60 s which exceed those that take place from 60 to 120 s, etc. This pattern of exponential decrease continues until durations extend to between 5 and 10 min, where performance falls to the levels that can be well sustained by the body's renewable aerobic sources of energy."

This is fact is easily noticeable when you watch a hockey game.

They also added the following statement: "The chemical energy available to the body from aerobic metabolism that fuels endurance efforts can be accurately quantified by measuring oxygen uptake at the mouth, but an equivalent technique for measuring the anaerobic chemical energy also released during sprint efforts presently does not exist."

That is why my team and I have moved from measuring on-ice VO_{2max} using a portable respiratory gas analyzer (measuring oxygen uptake at the mouth, as the authors indicated) to the use of biosensors and short-duration tests (no more than three minutes).

Lastly, they also note two important facts:

"… the greatest decrements in sprinting performance occur precisely during those very brief durations during which 1) the rates of anaerobic energy resupply to the contractile machinery are most rapid and 2) intracellular stores of chemical energy are greatest."

"Thus, the rate-limiting step in the release of chemical energy at the cellular level has been conclusively shown to be the contractile events that use the energy and not the metabolic pathways that resupply it."

Now, if you re-read the last sentenced I quoted from Matthew W. Bundle and Peter G. Weyand, you begin to have a good idea of why weight training is of so much importance in hockey. Without proper muscular training, you won't get the proper contractile capacity.

Before we take a look at how the performance of a hockey player progresses (or declines, depending on your perspective) on the ice, I would like to further discuss one important physiological aspect of high intensity effort: blood lactate.

What happens when a muscle contracts

Most of what has been learned about muscle contraction comes from the use of EMG (electromyography). Contracting muscles that allow you to move your body involve a voluntary action. Each muscle is controlled by what is called a motor unit. A motor unit is a nerve fiber coming from the brain that connects to some muscle fibers in a specific muscle. Each muscle is composed of many motor units that make contraction possible.

These motor units are recruited differently depending on the task you are performing. The more strength is required, the more motor units you will use and the firing rate (electrical activity of the muscle) will increase accordingly. Motor units are recruited from the weakest (low activation threshold) to the strongest (high activation threshold). After you've contracted a muscle group, you need to relax it. In the relaxation phase, the fibers that were not activated at the beginning of the contraction are still active for a certain period of time after the beginning of the relaxation phase. So, contraction and relaxation of a muscle group are two different actions.

There are three types of muscle contractions. First, isokinetic contractions involve sustaining a load in the same position with no joint movement. Second, isotonic contractions occur where there is joint movement as you apply a force against a constant resistance. Third, dynamic contractions occur where you apply a force against a variable resistance, such as in skating, where you contract your legs muscles to move your body against two significant resistant materials: the ice and the air.

The activation threshold of the muscle fibers is lower (they must act faster) and the firing rate is higher during dynamic contractions (like in skating). They demand more intensity. The demand (or intensity) related to skating is what makes it such a complex sport to understand.

Blood lactate

Should we care that much about blood lactate? Yes, but we should not *worry* so much about it and no longer consider it a metabolic waste. On a physiological level, when the exercise intensity reaches a point where your muscle cells use glucose without the presence of oxygen, you start producing blood lactate.

In the *Exercise physiology crash course* section, I mentioned that the anaerobic threshold (AT) is the power, or exercise intensity, at which you begin to produce blood lactate. In fact, this is an oversimplification.

As explained by Brooks et al.[6], it appears that during mild- to moderate-intensity exercise, lactate is formed, and in hard-intensity exercise, you guessed it, even more lactate is produced. In addition, muscle cells continuously consume and produce lactate. The highest consumption levels occur during exercise, when lactate levels increase. The net release of lactate underestimates the total amount of lactate that is produced by the working muscle. Lastly, the accumulation of blood lactate represents the anaerobic (with no oxygen) production of energy, since the consumption or removal of lactate is done under aerobic (with oxygen) conditions.

Metabolism and Nutrition

Your basal metabolic rate is the amount of energy you spend at rest. This energy is what your body requires just to maintain the functions of all of its organs.

The best way to measure your basal metabolic rate is in a lab like mine using a respiratory gas analyzer. It's the most precise way to do it. However, if you want to estimate your basal metabolic rate, you can do so using the formula provided below. But remember, the results will be *an estimate* and not a direct measure of your rate, and involves a margin of error (around 14 percent).

One of the most well-known formulas was introduced by Harris-Benedict[7] back in 1919. However, don't worry, many studies have demonstrated its validity for well-nourished individuals.

Formula for women:
Basal metabolic rate = 655 + (9.6 X your weight in kg) +
(1.8 X your height in cm) – (4.7 X your age).

Formula for men:
Basal metabolic rate = 66 + (13.7 X your weight in kg) +
(5 X your height in cm) – (6.8 X your age).

Let's say that your basal metabolic rate is estimated at 2,400 calories. This represents the energy required by the billions cells in your body to live (do their work). Now, as you exercise, your energy expenditure increases. Let's assume that today you've trained for three hours and spent 2,400 calories, and that you had to work, study, climb stairs, etc. during which you spent another 375 calories. Throughout your whole day, you spent 5,175 calories (2,400 + 2,400 + 375 = 5,175). That is a lot of energy.

Let's assume that you're not really paying too much attention to your nutrition and you only eat only 3,000 calories that day. You end up with a caloric deficit of 2,175 calories. Your body lacks 2,175 calories, so what will it do? Sacrifice some functions with a resulting decline in concentration, recovery, muscle regeneration, adaptation to training, cardiovascular adaptation, etc. In other words, your fitness level will drop, your performance will decline, you increase your risk of injury and you build up fatigue.

You must also balance your macronutrient intake (proteins, carbohydrates and lipids). So let's assume that 20 percent of your energy must come from proteins, 60 percent from carbohydrates and 20 percent from lipids. You must then remember that 1 gram of proteins provides 4 calories, 1 gram of carbohydrates provides 4 calories and 1 gram of lipids provides 9 calories. Therefore, if you distribute your 5,000 calories among these three categories (20 percent proteins; 60 percent carbohydrates and 20 percent lipids), you will need to eat 250 grams of proteins (5,000 X 20% = 1,000 calories; since 1 gram of proteins provides 4 calories, you divide 1,000 by 4, which gives you 250 grams of proteins), 750 grams of carbohydrates and 111 grams of lipids (remember that 1 gram of lipids equals 9 calories).

This is a really quick overview, but since this book is not about nutrition, I highly recommend that you consult a sports nutritionist. In my opinion, nutrition accounts for 60 percent of the results of your training program. If you don't eat properly, you can spend a lot of time training without any improvement. If you're serious about your sport, nutrition must be your number one priority with regard to training.

The notion of energy

At any moment in time, we all only have 100 percent of our energy available. At every moment of our lives, our brains must decide where to allocate this energy. Sometimes we can choose where and how we direct this energy, and other times, other factors interfere with our ability to do this. When we make a good decision, we reach a higher performance level and when we make a bad decision… well, you can guess what happens then.

The next figure is my way of illustrating what human performance is all about.

Figure 1. Human Performance Model

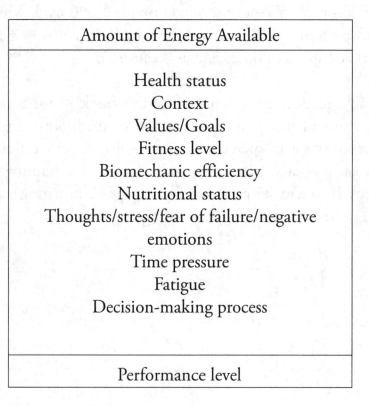

Amount of Energy Available
Health status
Context
Values/Goals
Fitness level
Biomechanic efficiency
Nutritional status
Thoughts/stress/fear of failure/negative emotions
Time pressure
Fatigue
Decision-making process
Performance level

Let's go through all of the points listed in Figure 1 and look at some examples of what can affect your performance level.

- Health status: You have a leg injury and you can't skate as fast as you normally do.
- Context: You have a hard time adapting to your new teammates.
- Values: Something has changed in your life and winning is no longer the number one priority.
- Goals: You pursue vague goals that don't allow you to define specific behaviors that will lead to success.
- Fitness level: Your fitness level is below what is expected, so it's impossible for you produce the amount of work that is required on the ice.
- Biomechanic efficency: You don't skate well enough to translate power into speed, so you spend a lot of energy without producing good results.
- Nutritional status: Your caloric intake is inadequate.
- Thoughts, stress, fear of failure, negative emotions: Your brain, which represents only 2 percent of your body weight, uses between 20 and 30 percent of your energy. If you don't know how to manage your brain and your emotions when facing difficult times it will suck your energy.
- Time pressure: The less time you have to do things, the more pressure builds up, which leads to lower accuracy and the emergence of incoherent actions.
- Fatigue: When recovery is not optimal, fatigue increases and performance declines.
- Decision making: If you can't think quickly and accurately under pressure, the energy you spend only leads to failure.

You must understand that proper training makes you fit and, as a result, you can become an excellent athlete. But as you can see, being a good hockey player takes a lot more than just being fit.

Overtraining and Recovery

In order to improve your fitness level, you train. Training represents a stress you impose on your body, to which it will respond by adapting to that stress (improving your fitness level). However, as mentioned above, it *is* a stress, and if this stress surpasses the capacity of your body to adapt, it becomes a negative stress. At this point, your body loses its capacity to respond positively to training, and you end up overtraining. You no longer have any more energy for training. Your fitness level decreases even if you continue the same training regimen. Nothing goes as planned when you're overtrained. Improvement is no longer possible.

Training for performance requires an athlete to remain close to a critical limit of intensity beyond which the athlete is at risk of experiencing negative consequences[8]. A training program in which the level of intensity is too low won't produce any benefits, and a program that is too intense can lead to overtraining. The proper balance can be sometimes difficult to achieve and maintain.

Contrary to what you might think, overtraining doesn't necessarily involve a loss of motivation. An athlete in a burned-out state does show this loss of motivation characteristic, but an overtrained athlete still has the will to improve.[9] However, overtraining has physical and psychological consequences:

- Fatigue
- Muscle pain
- Sleep disturbance
- Affective disorders
- Immune system perturbations
- Loss of appetite
- Allergic reactions
- Reduction of recovery capacity
- Performance decrement
- Negative impact on self-esteem
- Anxiety
- Loss of concentration

DR. DENIS BOUCHER, PH.D.

One important problem is the fact that many athletes tend to increase their training regimen when they feel no progress in their performance level. However, it has been shown that the main reason for the negative consequences resulting from a training program is omitting to include rest periods[8].

A poor performance during training and games is the first visible sign of overtraining. There are no standard biochemical, immunological and physiological markers for overtraining; it's a complex phenomenon. This also makes prevention more difficult.

The only way to try to prevent overtraining is to examine the psychological state of the player. It has been observed that mood and psychological state are highly sensitive to the intensity of the training program.[10]

It is also possible that the changes in psychological state observed during overtraining may not be the consequences of the problem, but rather its origin.[11]

If you want your body to improve your performance level and respond to training in an optimal manner, you must include rest periods in your program.

Summary

Now, let me wrap this all up to make everything clear.

1. You need a realistic and manageable performance goal.
2. You should evaluate your fitness level (more to come on this subject).
3. You need a good aerobic capacity (VO_{2max}). For a hockey player, a score of at least 53 is ideal; 60 is awesome, but anything higher does not produce any additional benefits.
4. Skating involves the recruitment of a large muscle mass and the decrement in performance is related to the contractile capacity of the working muscle.
5. Muscle strength and power are of utmost importance for hockey players.
6. Excellent skating technique is necessary to translate power into speed.
7. Fear, worry stress, anticipation and negative emotions have a negative impact on performance.
8. Include rest periods in your training program.

Dr. Denis Boucher, Ph.D.

CHAPTER 3
RESULTS FROM ON-ICE TESTING–A NEW LOOK AT FITNESS ON THE ICE

Here's a look at some tests we've conducted on the ice and what we have observed.

Power profile

First, let's take a look at what goes on when you skate as fast as you can for long periods (meaning between two and three minutes).

Tables 1, 2 and 3 (also identified as Player 1, 2 and 3) show the power profile generated by elite hockey players. What is important to observe is the fact that power decreases after a few seconds. The significant muscle mass required by skating at high intensities is responsible for the fast decrement in power.

Table 1. Player 1 - Results of an on-ice test performed by a professionnal hockey player

Run	Duration (s)	Speed (mph)	Power (W)	Power Ratio	Posture from Vert.
1	7.32	16.59	323	100.0%	40.1
2	7.97	15.24	268	82.5%	42.6
3	8.53	14.23	235	72.5%	40.8
4	9.11	13.32	208	64.1%	39.3
5	9.72	12.49	185	56.9%	32.2
6	9.95	12.20	177	54.5%	31.9
7	9.98	12.16	176	54.2%	32.0
8	10.63	11.42	157	48.3%	24.4
9	9.91	12.25	178	54.9%	21.3
10	10.95	11.10	149	45.9%	24.8
11	10.39	11.68	163	50.3%	23.4
12	11.06	10.97	146	44.9%	22.7
13	10.65	11.40	156	48.1%	26.6
14	11.04	10.99	146	45.0%	18.1
15	10.83	11.21	151	46.6%	24.1
16	10.67	11.37	156	47.9%	23.3
17	10.99	11.05	147	45.4%	22.7
18	11.31	10.73	140	43.1%	24.5
19	11.00	11.03	147	45.3%	21.1

Table 2. Player 2 - Results of an on-ice test performed by a hockey player before his participation at a training camp with an NHL team

Run	Duration (s)	Speed (mph)	Power (W)	Power Ratio	Posture from Vert.
1	8.05	15.29	266	100.0%	55.1
2	7.94	15.08	259	97.5%	48.2
3	8.32	14.58	244	91.6%	53.6
4	8.42	14.42	239	89.7%	56.8
5	9.18	13.23	203	76.4%	57.3
6	9.46	12.83	192	72.1%	57.1
7	11.03	11.03	145	54.6%	57.3
8	10.72	11.32	152	57.2%	58.3
9	10.63	11.42	155	58.1%	56.0
10	10.89	11.14	148	55.6%	56.5
11	11.29	10.75	139	52.0%	57.2
12	11.17	10.87	141	53.1%	56.2
13	11.02	11.01	145	54.4%	50.6
14	11.15	10.89	142	53.3%	51.0
15	11.75	10.33	129	48.4%	52.7
16	11.89	10.21	126	47.3%	53.5
17	11.64	10.43	131	49.2%	47.2
18	11.20	10.84	141	52.8%	53.5

Table 3. Player 3 - Results of an on-ice test performed by a highly ranked Quebec Junior Major Hockey League hockey player

Run	Duration (s)	Speed (mph)	Power (W)	Power Ratio	Posture from Vert.
1	7.48	16.22	296	100.0%	69.1
2	7.91	15.34	267	90.0%	62.9
3	8.50	14.28	233	78.6%	56.6
4	8.77	13.27	220	74.2%	52.4
5	9.64	12.59	184	62.2%	49.6
6	10.26	11.83	164	55.4%	44.4
7	10.62	11.42	154	51.9%	44.7
8	10.98	11.05	145	48.8%	40.7
9	11.46	10.59	134	45.1%	39.5
10	11.25	17.79	138	46.7%	40.0
11	11.20	10.83	140	47.1%	40.3
12	10.78	11.26	150	50.5%	40.4
13	11.12	10.91	141	47.7%	38.1
14	11.50	10.55	133	44.9%	37.8
15	11.54	10.52	132	44.6%	41.1
16	11.50	10.55	133	44.9%	34.6
17	10.78	11.26	150	50.5%	35.2
18	9.46	12.82	191	64.4%	59.9

As you can see, in Run 1 (Run = skating from one goal line to the other), Player 1 generates more power (323 watts) than Player 2 (266 watts) and 3 (296 watts). Also, Player 3 generates more power than Player 2.

If you look at the Power Ratio column, you can see that even though Player 1 generates the highest power, his power decreases quickly in the first five runs. You can also see that Player 2 maintains the highest power ratio in the first 5 runs. As a result, he maintains the highest power from Runs 3 to 6. So, in the first 50 seconds, Player 2 generates more power, even though he is less powerful than the other players in the first run.

Conclusion: the highest maximal power isn't the ultimate goal.

Speed Profile

If you look at the Speed column in Tables 2, 3 and 4 (our three players), you'll also notice that Player 2 maintains the highest speed profile in the first six runs (first 50 seconds). So, for short-term high intensity efforts, Player 2 wins.

Obviously, when power decreases, the speed you're able to reach also decreases. And, when you're skating, this happens quickly.

Maximal lactate steady state (critical power)

With regard to our three players, what happened in the first few seconds tells us that Player 2 is the player we are looking for. But, which player should we choose for skating bouts longer than 50 seconds?

The on-ice test we asked the players to perform also provides us with an important piece of informatio: the maximal lactate steady state (also known as critical power). This critical power is the highest power you can generate before accumulating blood lactate, which inevitably leads to exhaustion. Table 4 shows which of our players can sustain the highest power before entering the zone that will lead to exhaustion.

Table 4. Critical power of our three hockey players

Player	Critical power (in watts)	Percentage of maximal power
Player 1	144	44.6
Player 2	132	49.6
Player 3	139	46.8

Even though the percentage of the maximal power at which the critical power appears is the lowest with Player 1, he has the highest critical power off all three. The lowest percentage result is normal, since Player 1 generated the highest instant power (323 watts). Player 1 is the guy you will keep on the ice since the two other players will exhaust themselves before he does. After Run 6, Player 1 also maintained the highest speed.

From one leg to another

In this book, I will ask you to evaluate yourself and propose a training plan. This will include separate off-ice self-evaluation and training of your right and left legs. Why? Look at Table 5. You can see that, throughout the test, the right leg produces more acceleration than the left leg. These are the results of a player who thought he had fully recovered from an injury to his left knee. Even though he had made a complete physical recovery, you can see that his left leg was weaker than his right leg.

Even without the presence of injuries, we see this pattern with many players. One leg is weaker than the other. This is why you must train each leg separately. You need to achieve a proper balance.

Table 5. Acceleration produced by both legs on the ice

Run	Speed (mph)	Power (W)	Left	Right
1	15.04	259	(1.37)	1.45
2	15.48	273	(1.32)	1.54
3	14.96	257	(1.10)	1.46
4	14.46	242	(1.18)	1.34
5	13.75	211	(1.02)	1.23
6	13.10	200	(0.88)	1.21
7	12.94	196	(0.97)	1.06
8	12.26	176	(0.79)	0.96
9	11.98	168	(0.76)	0.91
10	12.05	171	(0.74)	0.92
11	11.80	165	(0.75)	0.94
12	11.82	165	(0.71)	0.81
13	11.81	165	(0.82)	0.96
14	11.98	162	(0.77)	0.94
15	11.49	157	(0.63)	0.74
16	11.55	159	(0.68)	0.84
17	11.79	158	(0.65)	0.85
18	11.73	156	(0.66)	0.82
19	12.75	156	(0.60)	0.83

Biomechanics: the science of translating power into speed

Table 6 illustrates the on-ice test results of 20 out of 35 players we tested. Under the Maximum Power column, you can see the results from the most powerful to the least powerful of the 20 players. The ranking goes from 1 to 20 in terms of the respective power generated. In the Maximum Speed column, the ranking is presented as a ratio. For example, 2/35 means the player has the second best score out of the 35 players in terms of speed reached on the ice. The speed in miles per hour is presented on the right side of the ranking.

It is interesting to note that the five most powerful players obtained the same ranking in terms of speed. However, you can see that Player 6, who ranked sixth for power generated (298 watts), slid down to tenth for maximum speed reached. For this player, power didn't translate into speed. This means his biomechanic efficiency isn't optimal. You can see the same pattern with Player 10, who ranked tenth for power, but only ranked fifteenth for speed reached. Then, if you look at Player 11, who obtained the same ranking as Player 10 for power (294 watts), he ranked ninth for speed. Player 11 shows better biomechanic efficiency, since he translated more power into speed than Player 10.

Biomechanics (your skating technique) is a key aspect of your performance. Even though you train seriously to become a powerful player, if you can't translate that power into speed, you won't get the results you expect.

Table 6. Power and speed ranking

Name	Maximum Power (W)		Maximum Speed (mph)	
	Ranking	Value	Ranking	Value
1	1	327	1/35	16.9
2	2	316	2/35	16.79
3	3	313	3/35	16.53
4	4	307	4/35	16.49
5	5	299	5/35	16.36
6	6	298	10/35	16.12
7	7	297	7/35	16.2
8	8	296	6/35	16.29
9	9	295	8/35	16.17
10	10	294	15/35	15.97
11	10	294	9/35	16.14
12	11	293	13/35	16.05
13	12	293	10/35	16.12
14	13	292	16/35	15.93
15	14	291	20/35	15.85
16	14	291	12/35	16.1
17	15	288	14/35	15.99
18	16	287	17/55	15.89
19	17	286	23/35	15.8
20	18	285	17/35	15.89

DR. DENIS BOUCHER, PH.D.

Why muscle training is important (power and muscle control)

Why is muscle training is important? I think you know the answer. Your skating performance is closely related to the capacity of your muscles to produce and maintain rapid and intense contractions.

You need muscle strength, but strength alone won't make you a fast and powerful skater. You need to contract your muscle cells quickly in order to produce power and reach higher speeds. Power is the product of force and contraction velocity.

You need to introduce the notion of muscle quality (which is defined as muscle strength and power normalized to muscle cross-sectional area). In one study, Reid and Fielding[12] observed that older persons with limited mobility showed 65 percent less muscle power and 13 percent less muscle mass when compared to healthy older adults. Compared to healthy middle-aged adults, they showed 95 percent less power and 35 percent less muscle mass. You can see that muscle power is affected to a greater degree than muscle mass. The authors suggest that with older adults, this huge discrepency in muscle power and mass indicates that factors other than muscle atrophy contribute to the loss of muscle power output among seniors with limited mobility. The notion of muscle quality therefore appears to be of great significance. They also underscore the impact of neuromuscular activation impairment on movement velocity and muscle coordination, which results in a reduction in the time it takes to reach peak force, which negatively affects muscle power.

You may be thinking, "I'm not old and I'm not limited, so what about me as a young (or young at heart) athlete?" Well, Tillin et al.[13] compared the neuromuscular performance of explosive athletes with untrained individuals. Before discussing their results, I need to introduce two important concepts: Electromechanical Demand (EMD) which is the time delay between the time the muscle receives the electrical command and the time it starts contracting, and the Rate of Force Development (RFD), which is how much and how fast you can produce force. These are the key factors that explain explosive contractions.

So, what did Tillin et al. discover? There were no differences in EMD when comparing the results of the athletes to the untrained subjects. However, they reported that the athletes showed greater synchronization in the activation onset of the contracting muscle. Athletes were 28 percent stronger than the untrained group, and they showed twice the RFD in the first 50 milliseconds of the contraction. However, the RFD of the untrained group was higher during the 50-100 millisecond time frame. So, if untrained individuals can generate a higher rate of force than trained athletes, but later in time, it seems that the higher power generated by athletes may not only be related to the contractile properties of the muscle-tendon unit, but to differences in neural activation as well.

Muscle power is extremely important in hockey. Strength is necessary to produce force. Contraction velocity is the most important variable in power production, and may be more related to neuromuscular efficiency.
The implications for your training program will be explained later.

What you need to build

Did I mention that hockey was the most physiologically complex sport? If we look at the physical qualities you need to build, you can understand why. To summarize, I have indicated that you need to build great:

- explosive power
- strength
- power
- anaerobic capacity
- aerobic capacity
- skating technique

I'll present the kind of training program that will help you get there later in this book. However, I want to emphasize that too many athletes look for THE type of training that will do it all. No matter what kind of training you do and or what name comes with it, if it isn't specific enough, you'll just be following a trend, unrealistically hoping for good results.

Before beginning your training program, I want you to understand what you will be doing.

To reach your maximal speed as fast as possible, you need explosive power (rate of force development for each contraction). This is more related to neuromuscular quality. As the seconds pass, your explosive power will decrease and you'll try to sustain a high power output (force X contraction velocity) for as long as possible (I always think in terms of seconds here). This is a physiologically weird zone where your muscle cells are not limited by the energy available (they have what they need) but by their contractile quality. Then, in a matter of seconds (35 to 45 seconds on average), you've lost 50 percent of your power and your speed has decreased acccordingly. You train to maintain the pace, and you're using your anaerobic reserves, you build up blood lactate and you'll naturally (within 50 to 60 seconds) reach the pace you can sustain without getting exhausted. After 50 seconds of skating, this is where a good aerobic capacity (VO_{2max}) is useful, because it allows you to sustain a higher demand for a longer period of time. As fatigue builds up, your skating takes a blow, you lose speed, and you try to compensate.

As you can see, in hockey, there is no single fitness factor.

Figures 2 and 3 illustrate what happens to power and speed while you skate your best over time.

Figure 2. Power profile over time

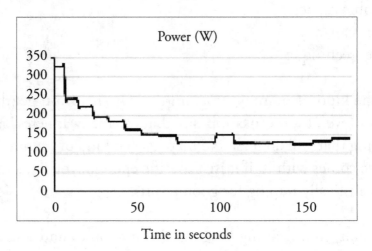

Time in seconds

Figure 3. Speed profile over time

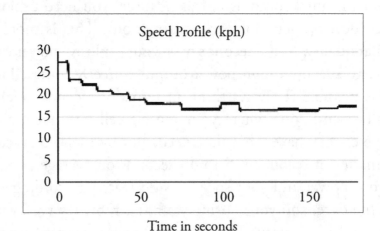

Time in seconds

Dr. Denis Boucher, Ph.D.

This is a pretty good summary of what goes on. But can we get a deeper understanding? Let's try.

Assuming you train properly off the ice, you develop strength, power, etc.; everything you think you need to be a great hockey player. But, on the ice, you combine power skating with contraction frequency. In short, instead of pushing your legs all the way through, thus reducing your stride frequency, you reduce your stride length and increase the frequency. It's like you are now jerking yourself across the rink. You may get a sense of speed, but it's only an impression because your legs are moving fast. You are not translating power into speed.

Contraction velocity and frequency are intertwined. You will reach a frequency where you lose power. In fact, it has been shown,[14] using hinged-blade ice skates, that increasing the duration of the push-off portion of the skating stance phase increases speed. So, longer contractions sometimes mean more speed on the ice. However, there's a balance to reach between velocity and frequency. Your leg muscle cells must contract quickly without sacrificing too much of the duration of the push-off phase, which you'll inevitably do at a certain stride frequency threshold.

Tables 7 and 8 show in how much time a less powerful versus a more powerful hockey player can push through a run (from one goal line to the other).

If we compare our two hockey players in the first three runs, we see that our less powerful player kept pushing off only 40.4, 36.6 and 36.9 percent of the total time duration for each run, while the other player (in much better shape) kept pushing off 61.2, 55 and 43 percent of the time. In the first three runs, the more powerful player produced an average of 256 watts for an average speed of 23.5 km/h (14.66 miles/h), while the less powerful player generated 248 watts for an average speed of 24.1 km/h (14.97 miles/h).

After the first three runs, however, our more powerful player (that is, initially more powerful) loses power and cannot keep pushing off any longer than our less powerful player. If we take a closer look, at the start of the fourth run, our less powerful player (that is, initially) produces more power than the other player and generally keeps pushing off for the same amount of time. He is now winning the race. The most powerful player only had an advantage for the first 25 seconds.

Would there be any benefit in training our less powerful player (if we can still describe him as such) to become more powerful? I don't think so. I would try to help him improve his performance in other areas, such as skating technique. For the most powerful player (or so he was initially), weight training, as per the program proposed in this book, would be of great help.

Table 7. Percentage of the total time a less powerful hockey player sustains power output for each run (acceleration time as a percentage of the total run)

Run	Duration (s)	Speed (kph)	Power (W)	Power Ratio	Acceleration Time (%)
1	8.02	25.01	276	100.0%	40.4%
2	8.54	23.70	250	90.4%	36.6%
3	9.19	22.05	218	79.0%	36.9%
4	9.78	20.45	190	68.7%	34.9%
5	10.41	19.55	175	63.2%	31.2%
6	11.16	18.14	152	55.1%	27.3%
7	11.68	16.92	134	48.5%	24.9%
8	11.83	16.53	128	46.5%	30.4%
9	11.60	16.50	128	46.3%	31.9%
10	11.41	17.15	137	49.7%	31.7%
11	11.66	17.10	137	49.4%	34.1%
12	11.18	16.39	126	45.8%	31.9%
13	10.44	18.87	164	59.2%	30.3%
14	10.28	18.57	159	57.5%	29.6%
15	10.11	19.42	173	62.5%	29.2%
16	10.79	19.22	169	61.3%	31.6%
17	5.89	16.98	135	48.8%	17.7%

Table 8. Percentage of the total time a physically fit hockey player sustains power output for each run (acceleration time as a percentage of the total run)

Run	Duration (s)	Speed (kph)	Power (W)	Power Ratio	Acceleration Time (%)
1	7.45	26.22	299	100.0%	61.2%
2	7.99	24.44	262	87.6%	55.0%
3	9.04	21.61	208	69.5%	43.0%
4	9.67	20.19	183	61.3%	33.2%
5	11.92	16.39	124	41.7%	26.1%
6	11.82	16.53	126	42.3%	23.0%
7	12.82	15.23	109	36.5%	24.2%
8	13.26	14.73	103	34.3%	30.6%
9	12.89	15.15	108	36.1%	32.7%
10	11.61	16.83	131	43.7%	30.2%
11	12.14	16.09	120	40.3%	32.2%
12	13.61	14.35	98	32.7%	30.3%
13	12.54	15.58	113	38.0%	25.2%
14	12.43	15.71	115	38.6%	32.8%
15	12.76	15.31	110	36.8%	21.4%

Now, let's take a look (Tables 9 and 10) at what goes on when your leg muscles lose their efficiency over time. Stride frequency versus power.

Table 9. Stride number and percentage of the total time a hockey player with a low fitness level sustains power output for each run

Run	Duration (s)	Speed (kph)	Power (W)	Power Ratio	Acceleration Time (%)	Stride number
1	8.10	24.79	269	100.0%	29.7%	11
2	8.48	23.50	243	90.5%	10.3%	14
3	8.79	22.56	225	83.8%	6.3%	16
4	9.14	21.88	213	79.1%	6.3%	16
5	9.48	20.90	195	72.7%	5.9%	16
6	9.68	20.33	185	69.0%	5.6%	18
7	9.99	20.03	180	67.1%	5.4%	18
8	10.12	19.07	165	61.3%	5.4%	19
9	9.89	19.55	172	64.2%	2.6%	18
10	10.23	19.95	179	66.6%	5.7%	17
11	10.51	18.43	155	57.5%	8.0%	19
12	10.61	18.72	159	59.2%	5.4%	18
13	10.47	18.13	150	55.8%	2.6%	19
14	10.49	19.19	167	62.0%	2.7%	17
15	10.71	18.10	150	55.7%	10.6%	19
16	10.67	18.38	154	57.2%	10.8%	19
17	10.63	18.25	152	56.5%	5.7%	18
18	5.19	18.48	155	57.8%	2.9%	17

Table 10. Stride number and percentage of the total time a hockey player with a very good fitness level sustains power output for each run

Run	Duration (s)	Speed (kph)	Power (W)	Power Ratio	Acceleration Time (%)	Stride number
1	7.46	26.17	299	100.0%	84.8%	11
2	7.63	25.59	286	95.8%	60.4%	11
3	8.46	23.08	236	78.9%	35.9%	12
4	9.03	21.63	209	70.0%	28.7%	13
5	10.03	19.48	172	57.6%	23.4%	15
6	10.13	19.29	169	56.5%	19.4%	15
7	10.79	18.10	150	50.3%	19.4%	16
8	10.89	17.93	148	49.4%	20.0%	15
9	11.03	17.70	144	48.3%	13.2%	15
10	11.27	17.33	139	46.4%	17.5%	15
11	10.57	18.48	156	52.3%	24.3%	14
12	11.20	17.44	140	47.0%	20.7%	15
13	11.09	17.62	143	47.8%	17.4%	14
14	10.40	18.78	161	53.8%	21.6%	15
15	10.51	18.58	158	52.8%	22.0%	13
16	12.13	16.11	121	40.6%	13.4%	16
17	11.12	17.56	142	47.6%	7.3%	14

You can see in Table 9 that the player with the lower fitness level increased his stride number from the second run, and that the percentage of time he could maintain his acceleration dropped dramatically. From Runs 3 to 8, he kept accelerating for only about 6 percent of the total time it took him to cross the ice rink. Thus, 94 percent of his effort time was dedicated to maintaining the speed gained. From the 14 to 19 strides it took him to cross the rink, the power he generated kept decreasing (225 to 165 watts, from Runs 3 to 8). He evidently moved his legs faster. This raises the question: Is this a good thing?

Now, what happened to our other hockey player in much better shape (Table 10)? He kept accelerating for a far longer period of time (84.8 percent of the total time in the first run, and maintained an acceleration of about 20 percent for most of the duration of the test). He increased his stride frequency, but not as much as the other player (with a lower fitness level). So, he kept pushing for longer periods of time and it took him fewer strides to cross the ice rink (so we assume that the duration of the push-off stance phase was longer). This seems like a much better way to skate, don't you think? Let's dig a little deeper before coming to a conclusion on this.

From Run 4 to the end of the test, our player with the lower fitness level generated more power and speed than our player with a good fitness level. What happened here? Simply put, it appears in this case that increasing stride frequency and reducing the duration of the acceleration time produced more power and more speed in the long run (after 25 seconds). In the first 25 seconds, the player with the best fitness level won, but in the long run, the fewer strides (which involved a longer push-off phase) combined with a longer acceleration time, translated into more power and speed on the ice. After that, each stride generated less power compared to the other player who increased his stride frequency and reduced his acceleration time.

I do believe, however, that no single skating technique fits every player. There may be many more variables that influence skating power and speed that we initially thought.

You need to train off the ice, but all this training must translate into better performance on the ice. If you don't know what will make you a better athlete on the ice, you will waste your precious training time, because the results off the ice won't translate on the ice.

Training is a continuum of activities that must make you a better athlete… *on* the ice.

CHAPTER 4
BODY COMPOSITION AND FITNESS EVALUATION

You want to become a great athlete, so you must follow a "surgical" training program, not the kind of general-purpose "one-size-fits-all" program that everybody is following, hoping for the best possible results. I will outline what I believe are the most important rules to follow in designing your training program, as well as how to address these rules.

A word about body composition

Why is it so important to monitor your body composition? Because if you have a high percentage of body fat, for example, it will slow you down. Body fat doesn't produce work; it's inert. Since you have to carry it around, it slows you down and contributes to the premature onset of fatigue. Would you go on the ice with a 25-pound backpack? No! Well, if you're 25 pounds overweight, you're doing the same thing.

The body fat percentage of most professional hockey players I have tested varies between 7 and 11 percent. A body fat percentage of no more than 12 is ideal. Anything less than 7 percent, however, can be counterproductive.

When you step on the scale, the reading gives you your total weight. However, this number doesn't tell you much about the different structures of your body. Yet, this is important information to have and analyze. In fact, your total body weight is the sum of five levels, as described by Shen et al.[15]

The atomic level includes the billions of atoms that make up our bodies: oxygen, carbon, hydrogen, nitrogen and other elements.

The molecular level refers to the concentration of water, lipids, proteins, minerals, glucose and other molecules in the body.

At the cellular level, we look at body content in terms of extracellular fluids, solids and the cells (and adipocytes).

At the tissue-organ level, we consider global structures: bones, skeletal muscle, adipose tissue, visceral organs and remaining tissues.

Lastly, at the whole-body level, we add up what your body is composed of from what we can see: trunk, head, upper and lower body.

Stepping on the scale only gives you information about the latter level: the sum of what your body is made of. Any variation in your total weight doesn't give you any indication as to what this variation is related to. The bathroom scale is not a particularly useful instrument.

There are many ways to evaluate your body composition. As suggested above, stepping on the scale is actually the worst thing to do. Skinfold measurement (using a skinfold caliper) is easy to do, but I'm personally not too fond of this method, because it doesn't give me the level of precision I'm looking for. Some types of ultrasound guns are designed to measure skinfold thickness. They're something of a modern version of skinfold calipers. I have tried them, and I'm not much of a fan of those either.

The gold standard–hydrostatic weighing–is a very precise method, but not suitable for most labs and clinics because the equipment itself doesn't make it a fast and easy method to use.

My favorite method of evaluating body composition is with bioimpedance scales. I've been using this method for many years now. Even though many factors (such as variation in body water content) can affect the results, some scales produce highly accurate and valid results. These scales give you precise readings of your total weight, lean body mass, fat mass and water content. This is my favorite way of measuring gains in lean mass (of which muscle mass is an important part).

Other more sophisticated methods are available in hospitals and research labs (DEXA, Tomography, Magnetic Resonance Imaging, Doubly-Labelled water) but are obviously not easily accessible.

Overall, this is why I like to use bioimpedance scales. Manufacturers such as Omron, Tanita and Withins (I want to clearly state that I have no involvement or affiliation with any these companies) produce good, reliable and affordable scales.

Evaluate your fitness level

Once again, if you want to improve your performance, you first need to know where you stand in terms of physical fitness. With this knowledge, you can then build a training program designed to help you develop the physical qualities you need.

Here are the test protocols I invite you to follow.

Testing explosive power (on the ice)

Here's a very simple test you can do yourself. Stand still at the goal line of your choice. Ask someone to start a count down. You then explode and skate as fast as you can towards the other goal line. You'll need another partner to record when you arrive so you can measure the time it took to cross the ice as accurately as possible. The faster you get, the more powerful you will become. But, you must remember that your skating technique plays an important role in terms of the speed you can generate.

Testing muscle strength (off the ice)

Muscle strength is the force that a muscle can generate in a single maximal effort. Muscle strength is a component of muscle power (force X speed at which you apply that force over a specific distance).

Let's start with the protocol and then look the muscle groups you can test.

Protocol

- ✓ On a bike, do a 10-minute aerobic warm-up at moderate intensity.
- ✓ For the muscle group to be tested, perform a set of 10 repetitions using a weight equal to about 50 percent of your expected 1RM (maximal load you expect to move in 1 repetition).
- ✓ Then, perform a set of 5 repetitons with a weight approximately 75 percent of your expected 1RM.
- ✓ Take a 3- to 5- minute rest period.

- ✓ Do 1 repetition at 90 to 95 percent of your estimated 1RM.
- ✓ Take a 3- to 5- minute rest period.
- ✓ Do a 1RM repetition. If you've succeeded…
- ✓ Take a 3- to 5- minute rest period.
- ✓ Increase the weight while respecting the protocol until you can't increase the load any more.

IMPORTANT: Make sure that when you execute the movement, you don't compensate with your body. You need to evaluate the strength of the specific muscle group you're testing, not the strength of that muscle group when you try to bring the rest of your body to the rescue. Always think about injury prevention. Your goal is not to injure yourself.

You can thus evaluate specific muscle groups using this protocol. Here are the most important muscle groups I invite you to test. You can do the test every 2, 3 or 4 months to evaluate the impact of your training program.

Follow the strength testing protocol guidelines. Test each leg. Photos for each exercise can be found in the Exercises chapter of the book.

Use the following table to record your results.

Table 11. My strength results

Exercise	Muscle group	1RM
Leg extension	Quadriceps	Right Left
Leg curl	Hamstrings	Right Left
Hip flexion	Hip flexors	Right Left
Squat	Quadriceps-gluteal region	
Calf raise	Calves	Right Left
Barbell bench press	Pectoral region-deltoids-triceps	
Biceps curl	Biceps	
Triceps extension	Triceps	
Lat. pull down	Large dorsal muscle (latissimus dorsi)	

Testing muscle power (the speed-strength continuum)—off the ice

Muscle power is the capacity to move a load with speed over a specific distance. Muscle power is what you use to accelerate on the ice and reach top speed. On the ice, you use many muscle groups. Here, you will test them individually.

For each muscle group presented below, you will test your speed-strength continuum. Generally speaking, a load representing 70 percent of your 1RM corresponds to the maximal power you can generate. Around 40 percent of your 1RM represents the load at which you produce your maximal contraction speed.

So, you will test different loads for each muscle group.

Dr. Denis Boucher, Ph.D.

Protocol

Now, here's the protocol to follow.

- ✓ On a bike, do a 10-minute aerobic warm-up at moderate intensity.
- ✓ For the muscle group to be tested, perform a set of 15 repetitions using a weight equal to about 30 percent of 1RM (maximal load you expect to move in 1 repetition).
- ✓ Take a 2-minute rest period.
- ✓ Again, for the muscle group to be tested, perform a set of 12 repetitions using a weight equal to about 50 percent of your 1RM.
- ✓ Test each muscle group using a weight representing 70 percent of your 1RM. You must contract the muscle group as fast as you can.
- ✓ Take a 30-minute rest period and repeat the same procedure with a load of 50 percent of your 1RM.
- ✓ Take a day off.
- ✓ Repeat the warm-up procedure and test each muscle group using a weight that represents 40 percent of your 1RM. (Warm-up procedure: On a bike, do a 10-minute aerobic warm-up at moderate intensity.)
- ✓ For the muscle group to be tested, perform a set of 15 repetitions using a weight equal to about 30 percent of 1RM (maximal load you expect to move in 1 repetition.
- ✓ Take a 2-minute rest period.
- ✓ Again, for the muscle group to be tested, perform a set of 12 repetitions using a weight equal to about 50 percent of your 1RM.)

When you do the test, you must calculate the number of repetitions and the amount of time you were able to sustain the contractions. For example, during leg extension at 50 percent of 1RM, you completed 18 repetitions in 40 seconds. Write down these two results in the appropriate Table.

Note that I suggest you do the test with your lower body muscle groups. You can also do it with your upper body muscle groups as described in the strength testing protocol.

Follow the speed-strength (power) testing protocol guidelines. Test each leg. Photos for each exercise can be found in the Exercises chapter of the book.

Use the following table to record your results.

Table 12. My speed-strength (power) results

Exercise	Muscle group	70% of 1RM #Reps	Time (sec.)
Leg extension (Right)	Quadriceps		
Leg extension (Left)	Quadriceps		
Leg curl (Right)	Hamstrings		
Leg curl (Left)	Hamstrings		
Hip flexion (Right)	Hip flexors		
Hip flexion (Left)	Hip flexors		
Squat	Quadriceps-gluteal region		
Calf raise (Right)	Calves		
Calf raise (Left)	Calves		

Exercise	Muscle group	50% of 1RM #Reps	Time (sec.)
Leg extension (Right)	Quadriceps		
Leg extension (Left)	Quadriceps		
Leg curl (Right)	Hamstrings		
Leg curl (Left)	Hamstrings		
Hip flexion (Right)	Hip flexors		
Hip flexion (Left)	Hip flexors		
Squat	Quadriceps-gluteal region		
Calf raise (Right)	Calves		
Calf raise (Left)	Calves		

Exercise	Muscle group	40% of 1RM	
		#Reps	Time (sec.)
Leg extension (Right)	Quadriceps		
Leg extension (Left)	Quadriceps		
Leg curl (Right)	Hamstrings		
Leg curl (Left)	Hamstrings		
Hip flexion (Right)	Hip flexors		
Hip flexion (Left)	Hip flexors		
Squat	Quadriceps-gluteal region		
Calf raise (Right)	Calves		
Calf raise (Left)	Calves		

Testing time frame

Strength and speed-strength (power) are two protocols that I recommend you do in the same week. Table 13 charts the protocols over time in such a way as to prevent fatigue and get the best possible results.

Table 13. Testing time frame

Day 1	Day 2	Day 3	Day 4	Day 5
AM Explosive power on the ice PM Strength testing	Rest	Speed-strength testing First test at 70% of 1RM Take a 30-minute rest Second test at 50% of 1RM	Rest	Speed-strength testing Third test at 40% of 1RM Repeat the warm-up procedure before doing the test.

CHAPTER 5
BUILDING YOUR TRAINING PROGRAM

Warming up

Warming up is used to prepare your muscles and joint structures to sustain the high physical demands you will experience on the ice. This is essential to help prevent injuries.

Warming up is also a way to influence the physiological responses of your body before you go on the ice.

A warm up usually involves stretching combined with light to moderate aerobic exercises (cycling or jogging). I suggest beginning with some stretching exercises, and then I will introduce you to the notion of "Priming".

Stretching

Stretching Workout			
Exercise	**Sets**	**Reps**	**Tempo**
Shoulder Stretching	1	1	30 sec
Back Buttocks And Thigh Stretching	1	1	30 sec
Leg Gluteal Stretch	1	1	30 sec
Abdominal Oblique	1	1	30 sec
Anterior Shoulder Pectoral Flexibility	1	1	30 sec
Thigh And Back Stretching	1	1	30 sec
Back / Hamstrings Stretch	1	1	30 sec
Back Buttocks Flexibility	1	1	30 sec
Back Flexibility	1	1	30 sec
Back Flexibility / Trunk Rotation	1	1	30 sec
Back Leg Flexibility	1	1	30 sec
Back Swiss Ball Stretching - On The Back	1	1	30 sec
Back Swiss Ball Stretching - On The Belly	1	1	30 sec
Back Swiss Ball Stretching - On The Side	1	1	30 sec
Back Stretching	1	1	30 sec
Adductors Machine	1	1	30 sec
Back Stretching	1	1	30 sec
Back Trunk Stretching	1	1	30 sec
Neck Range Of Motion - On The Front	1	1	30 sec
Neck Range Of Motion - On The Side	1	1	30 sec
Quadriceps Stretching	1	1	30 sec
Seated Forward Flexion	1	1	30 sec
Calf / Buttocks Flexibility	1	1	30 sec
Ankle Range Of Motion	1	1	30 sec
Swiss Ball Flexibility Leg	1	1	30 sec

Priming

As mentioned above, warming up serves as a means of modifying the physiological responses of your body before you go on the ice. The real goal is to delay the time of onset of exhaustion. If you adequately prepare your body, you'll see a huge improvement in your performance on the ice.

I have started using "priming exercises" as described by Burnley et al.[16] These sport scientists studied the impact of a heavy and severe period of exercise (6 minutes) before completing an exercise protocol leading to exhaustion. They found that a heavy-intensity 6-minute bout of aerobic activity (cycling in this case) increases exercise tolerance by delaying time to exhaustion. The way to calculate the heavy intensity zone is quite complex to explain. When I can use specific measurements in my lab, I recommend that players get on a bike and complete a 6-minute bout of exercise at around 80 to 85 percent of their maximal heart rate (max heart rate = 220 - your age). Although I am aware that the margin of error is greater using this method, we must occasionally live with it when it's not possible to conduct the proper testing. Above that intensity level, no benefits can be gained.

What is interesting is that this strategy is counter-intuitive. In fact, the general belief among athletes and trainers is that it is best not to deplete too much energy before a performance. That's right! Old thinking isn't always correct.

So, warming-up serves two purposes:

- preparing your body (preventing injury);
- delaying the onset of fatigue (manipulating your physiological reactions).

Weight training

The training program I will present here addresses the musclar qualities you need to have to become a great athlete: explosive power, strength and speed-strength (power). The training program involves training muscles or muscle groups in a localized manner (every muscle or muscle group trained individually). However, the purpose of this training program is to allow you to perform better on the ice by allowing you to reach an excellent aerobic capacity (VO_{2max} on the ice of 53 and above), great anaerobic power (maximal lactate steady state or critical power) above 45 percent of your maximal power and great contractile quality (sustaining muscle contraction under high physical demands).

To better understand what you should see on the ice, Table 14 is a sample of the type of report we give hockey players after a test conducted on the ice.

The graphs present the evolution throughout the all-out on-ice test of the speed profile, heart rate, power, breathing rate, breathing rate and breathing amplitude ratio, and breathing amplitude. This is our way of getting a quick overview of what happened during the test on a physiological and biomechanical level.

Overall, you can see that speed and power declined throughout the test and essentially reached a steady state from 60 to 150 seconds. The heart reached a climax in the first 20 seconds. The breathing rate also reached a climax in the first 20 seconds of the test but declined after that point. The breathing rate (your way of drawing oxygen in the lungs and into the blood stream) decreased. Since the need for oxygen kept increasing, it had to be compensated by an increase in breathing amplitude (torso inflation).

The Heart Rate table provides the following information: predicted maximal heart rate, maximal heart rate reached in the test, heart rate reserve (heart rate reserve = maximal predicted heart rate – maximal heart rate reached during the test), and the estimated VO_{2max} (wearing hockey gear = an average of 24 lbs) on the ice. We assume that when the heart rate reserve is 15 and above, the maximal heart rate hasn't been reached. Two reasons may explain this:

poor effort or the biomechanical demands of the test were so high for the player that he was unable to reach his maximal physiological capacity. The legs gave out before the heart, lungs and muscle cells could reach their maximal potential. Then, to make it through the test, the player had to considereably decrease his power and speed. We then see an emerging mismatch between the biomechanical demands and the player's physiological adaptation. The legs' muscles couldn't sustain the high demand.

Getting back to the results shown in Table 14 (in the Heart Rate table), the estimated VO_{2max} of 51 indicates good aerobic capacity.

In the Power table (W), you see the maximal power generated on the ice (at 299 watts), the critical power (or maximal lactate steady state) at 140 watts, representing a ratio of 47 percent of the maximal power (299 watts), the total work performed (in kilojoules), and the work above end power (WEP) (also presented in kilojoules). I won't get into the notion of work and WEP because it won't be of much use for the purpose of this book. So, our player generated a maximal power of 299 watts, and the critical power appeared at 140 watts (or 47 percent of the maximal power [140÷ 299]). This indicates a good anaerobic capacity (above 45 percent is good to excellent).

In the Time to Exhaustion table, you see that the average speed at critical power was 17.44 km/h. So, when the player exceeds 140 watts or 17.44 km/h, the intensity of the effort will inevitably lead him to exhaustion. Since we can calculate the time to exhaustion, if we ask our player to skate at his maximal speed (26.17 km/h) we know that he can only last around 29 to 30 seconds before complete exhaustion sets in. This is really useful information, as you can imagine.

The last table presents the results for every run (from one goal line to the other). This is a good way to dissect the power and speed profile in terms of duration (seconds) and see how fast the player loses power after every run. You can see that the player lost only 4 percent of his power in the second run, but his power quickly declined by 21 percent in the third run, 30 percent in the fourth and 50 percent in the seventh.

Dr. Denis Boucher, Ph.D.

Looking at this information in terms of seconds, we can see that the player could maintain a near maximal power level for about 15 seconds during the first two runs. From seconds 15 to 23.6, he lost 21 percent of his power. After 52 seconds (Run 7) he lost 50 percent of his power.

This allows us to analyze the power and speed profile in more detail and better compare the evolution of the player from test to test. More importantly, it's the best way to assess whether your training program has had a positive impact on your performance on the ice.

What is amazing is that we gather the biomechanical information (power, speed and posture) using an application we developed. You skate with your cell phone strapped to your chest and that's it. To connect all that with physiological data (heart rate, breathing rate, breathing amplitude) we couple a chest band or a smart textile shirt to the app, and we're all set; everything about you is instantly revealed (in terms of performance on the ice, of course).

Table 14. On-ice testing report

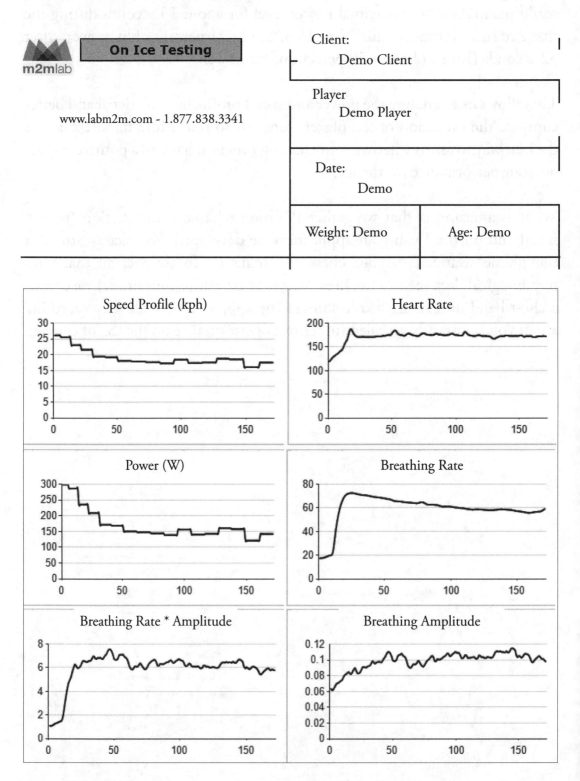

On Ice Testing m2mlab www.labm2m.com - 1.877.838.3341	Client: Demo Client
	Player Demo Player
	Date: Demo
	Weight: Demo	Age: Demo

Speed Profile (kph)

Heart Rate

Power (W)

Breathing Rate

Breathing Rate * Amplitude

Breathing Amplitude

Heart Rate			Power (W)			Time to Exhaustion	
Predicted:	201		Max. Power:	299		Max Speed: 29.62 sec. at 26.17 kph	
Maximum:	188		Critical Power:	140		Avg Speed at CP: 17.44 kph	
Reserve:	13		Ratio Pmax:	47.0%			
Est. VO2max:	51		Work (KJ):	28.5			
			WEP (KJ):	4.7			

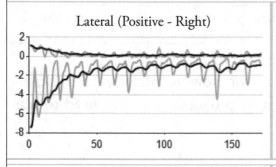

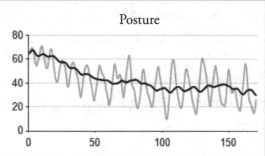

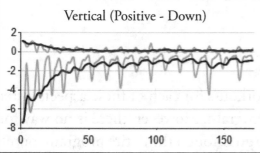

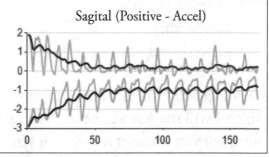

Run	Duration (s)	Speed (kph)	Power (W)	Power Ratio	Accel Time (%)	Steps	Heart Rate (bpm)	Breathing Rate (bpm)	Breathing Ampl. (mV)	Left	Right	Posture
1	7.46	26.17	299	100.0%	84.8%	11	126	17.8	0.06	(4.62)	0.82	65.2
2	7.63	25.59	286	95.8%	60.4%	11	142	24.5	0.08	(4.11)	0.64	61.7
3	8.46	23.08	236	78.9%	35.9%	12	177	62.8	0.09	(2.46)	0.32	56.2
4	9.03	21.63	209	70.0%	28.7%	13	171	72.2	0.09	(2.11)	0.22	49.3
5	10.03	19.48	172	57.6%	23.4%	15	171	70.6	0.10	(1.82)	0.21	45.4
6	10.13	19.29	169	56.5%	19.4%	15	174	68.9	0.10	(1.32)	0.17	42.2
7	10.79	18.10	150	50.3%	19.4%	16	178	66.6	0.10	(1.25)	0.07	39.7
8	10.89	17.93	148	49.4%	20.0%	15	175	64.7	0.09	(1.36)	0.15	42.7
9	11.03	17.70	144	48.3%	13.2%	15	177	64.0	0.10	(1.27)	0.12	38.8
10	11.27	17.33	139	46.4%	17.5%	15	176	62.2	0.10	(0.97)	0.08	34.4
11	10.57	18.48	156	52.3%	24.3%	14	176	60.9	0.11	(1.03)	0.26	32.7
12	11.20	17.44	140	47.0%	20.7%	15	176	59.4	0.10	(0.91)	0.12	37.3
13	11.09	17.62	143	47.8%	17.4%	14	173	58.6	0.10	(0.86)	0.14	33.0
14	10.40	18.78	161	53.8%	21.6%	15	170	58.4	0.11	(1.27)	0.13	42.5
15	10.51	18.58	158	52.8%	22.0%	13	173	58.5	0.11	(1.40)	0.14	34.8
16	12.13	16.11	121	40.6%	13.4%	16	173	56.6	0.10	(0.80)	0.09	32.2
17	11.12	17.56	142	47.6%	7.3%	14	172	57.1	0.10	(1.03)	0.17	32.4

Maximum Power
Good maximal power of 299 watts or 1.41 watts/lb at an average speed of 19.02 (kph).
Critical Power
Critical power appears at 46.97% of the maximal power at an average speed of 17.44 (kph). This indicates an excellent anaerobic capacity.
Estimated VO2$_{max}$
VO2$_{max}$ is estimated at 51.01 mlO2/kg/min (weight with equipment). This is a good maximal oxygen uptake.

Now that you have an overall picture of how to analyze your skating performance, let's go back to your training program. You thus need to train for:

- explosive power;
- strength;
- speed-strength (power).

I will introduce the different training workouts for each of these aspects, after which I will suggest a general training program. However, there is no way for me to tell you whether it's wise for you to go through the entire program. Some of you may have excellent explosive power, and just maintaining your current level would be fine. Going through the entire explosive training portion of the program could be a waste of time. Nevertheless, it will give you an overview on how to prepare yourself.

CHAPTER 6
THE TRAINING PROGRAM

Overview

The training program will manipulate the followng variables:

- duration
- type of training
- number of sessions per week
- number of minutes of training per session
- muscle groups to train
- number of sets
- number of repetitions per set
- tempo
- recovery between sets

All of these variables can be manipulated in order to improve your fitness level. It's a structure. However, you shouldn't see it as a fixed structure. Remember, every variable can be manipulated. The program presented here is one way of structuring a training program. Over time, this structure must evolve along with you.

Table 15. Training calendar

Day 1	Day 2	Day 3	Day 4	Day 5	Day 6	Day 7
Muscular (1 hour) + aerobic training (1 hour)	Muscular (75 minutes)	Aerobic (1 hour)	Rest	Muscular (75 minutes) + aerobic (45 minutes)	Muscular (75 minutes)	Stretching

This calendar represents a maximum of 7.5 hours of training per week.

Aerobic training

Since this book is more about weight training, I just want to specify that, in my opinion, long-distance training is not that useful. Your aerobic training program should vary between 45 and 60 minutes per session. You should vary your training between short-term intervals, long-term intervals, and at higher and lower intensities.

THE TRAINING PROGRAM ON A WEEKLY BASIS

A few notions to remember

You must remember that strength helps you produce force. Power is the capacity to exert force in the shortest possible time. Explosive power represents the rate of force you generate in the first milliseconds of the muscular contraction.

Also, when I refer to a percentage of 1RM, this is where the results of your strength test will be useful.

To improve power, I recommend that you do all of your repetitions at high velocity when you work on this aspect. **You must absolutely maintain control over your movement at all times**. You must be serious about this. **Your movement must be full and complete every time**. When your muscle can't contract anymore during a full and complete range of motion, you're done. Do not try to compensate by contorting your body and grimacing.

Adjusting your program to your needs

As I mentioned above, your program shouldn't be viewed as static. It must evolve with you and, over time, some portions may no longer be useful to you. To illustrate this, we followed a team of players we tested on the ice and generated the kind of complex reports presented in this book. However, to simplify the training process, I summarized the reports to the coach as illustrated in Tables 16 to 20.

In these tables, *Biomechanic efficiency (High)* is the highest power/speed ratio (max power divided by max speed) recorded in the first 25 seconds; and *Biomechanic efficiency (Low)* represent the lowest power/speed ratio recorded from second 25 to the end of the test.

Table 16. Training recommendations following an on-ice test

Quality	Results	Goal
Max power (Watts)	284	Improve by 5%
Anaerobic power (Watts)	153- (53.8%)	Maintain
Aerobic power V_{O2Max}	44	Improve by 12%
Biomechanic Efficiency (High) Ratio power/speed	11.20	Improve explosive speed by 3 to 5%
Biomechanic Efficiency (Low) Ratio power/speed	8.36	Improve speed after 25 sec by 3 to 5%

For this player, weight training should account for 40 percent of his total training time to give him greater strength and explosive power. The remaining 60 percent of his training time should be dedicated to aerobic training in order to improve his VO_{2max}.

Table 17. Training recommendations following an on-ice test

Quality	Results	Goal
Max power (Watts)	272	Improve by 10%
Anaerobic power (Watts)	133-(48.9%)	Improve by 4 to 5%
Aerobic power V_{02Max}	60	Maintain
Biomechanic Efficiency (High) Ratio power/speed	10.76	Improve explosive speed by 8%
Biomechanic Efficiency (Low) Ratio power/speed	8.00	Improve speed after 25 sec by 10%

This player has a really high VO_{2max} but not enough muscular contractile qualities, since he needs to improve his maximal power, his anaerobic power and his biomechanic efficiency.

For this player, I recommend that he spend 70 percent of his training time on weight training and 30 on aerobic training in order to maintain his current aerobic capacity (just keep doing what he does).

For this player, I would suggest following the program suggested later in this book.

Table 18. Training recommandations following an on-ice test

Quality	Results	Goal
Max power (Watts)	241	Improve by 15%
Anaerobic power (Watts)	119-(49.4%)	Improve by 10%
Aerobic power V_{02Max}	44	Improve by 12 to 15%
Biomechanic Efficiency (High) Ratio power/speed	10.28	Improve explosive speed by 10%
Biomechanic Efficiency (Low) Ratio power/speed	7.54	Improve speed after 25 sec by 15%

This player needs to work hard and strategically because he needs to improve his aerobic and muscular qualities in general. He needs to go through the training program I suggest in this book, and make sure he improves his aerobic and anaerobic power (or capacity). I would recommend a 50-50 training approach, where 50 percent of his activities focus on aerobic training and 50 percent on muscular training.

Table 19. Training recommandations following an on-ice test

Quality	Results	Goal
Max power (Watts)	299	Maintain
Anaerobic power (Watts)	140-(47.0%)	Maintain
Aerobic power V_{02Max}	51	Improve by 5%
Biomechanic Efficiency (High) Ratio power/speed	11.42	Maintain
Biomechanic Efficiency (Low) Ratio power/speed	8.08	Improve speed after 25 sec by 5%

This player shows really good muscular contractile qualities. Maximal power, anaerobic power and biomechanic efficiency (High) are excellent. However, he loses a lot of his biomechanic efficiency after 25 seconds. I recommend that this player invest 40 percent of his training time on improving his aerobic power. The remaining 60 percent of his training should focus on muscular training in order to improve his long-term (over 25 seconds) muscular contractile qualities. Also, spending time on improving his skating technique would be a strategic move.

Table 20. Training recommandations following an on-ice test

Quality	Results	Goal
Max power (Watts)	330	Maintain
Anaerobic power (Watts)	171-(51.7%)	Maintain
Aerobic power V_{O2Max}	55	Maintain
Biomechanic Efficiency (High) Ratio power/speed	11.98	Maintain
Biomechanic Efficiency (Low) Ratio power/speed	9.03	Maintain

This is a really efficient player. He just needs to maintain what he has gained so far. I would recommend that this player continue his current training program. Looking for any aerobic or muscular improvement at this point would be a waste of time. He could invest more time on improving other hockey skills.

INSTRUCTIONS BEFORE YOU BEGIN YOUR PROGRAM

If you have muscle or joint problems, health problems, cardiovascular or pulmonary conditions, health risk factors such as smoking, hypertension, diabetes, high cholesterol, stress, or experience fatigue and shortness of breath, **you must first obtain the consent of your physician before beginning this training program.**

Pre-training warm-up
You should do around 10 minutes of aerobics (bike, treadmill, walk or elliptical) at a low intensity to increase blood flow and help warm up your muscles. This helps prevent injury and will enhance the quality of your training.

When to stop an exercise
Never push beyond your capacities, or you will tend to compensate by changing body position, which increase the risk of injury.

Stop your movement at the first sign of muscular fatigue. Don't to try to surpass your limits, since you have nothing to gain by doing this. Respect your body's limits. Once muscular fatigue sets in and your movement becomes more difficult to control, it is time to stop exerting yourself, *even if you haven't completed the suggested number of repetitions.*

Terms used in your training program
Several terms are used in the presentation of your training program.

Weeks
Your program is planned over a certain number of weeks.

Set
The number of times you must perform the same number of repetitions of a given exercise.

Repetition
The number of times you repeat the same exercise.

Weight

Since I cannot evaluate the weights you should be working with, I have indicated a percentage of the maximal load to work with. Sometimes, you will see the mention "S" (for "See note") to refer you to more specific information on the maximal load you should be working with.

The percentage of the maximal load is a way to help you determine which loads you should be using. For example, if you feel you can lift a 100-lb load in one repetition during arm flexion (biceps), 65 percent of the maximal load means you should be working with a 65-lb weight.

Another, simpler way to look at it is if your program includes 3 sets of 15 to 20 repetitions at 40 percent of your maximal capacity, this means that you just have to find the weight that will allow you to do 15 to 20 repetitions for a given muscle group.

You will probably have to go through a few training sessions before you can more specifically determine which weights are appropriate for you.

Frequency

The number of suggested training sessions per week.

Maintain

Some exercises must be completed in a static manner; that is, while maintaining a certain position. For example, when 45 seconds are indicated, I am asking you to maintain the position for 45 seconds. The suggested time is a goal. Don't worry if can't go longer than 25 seconds. You will make progress throughout the program.

Tempo

Tempo is the speed at which you perform a movement. The duration of the movement is important, since it determines the level of tension exerted on the muscle. A tempo of 2-0-2 indicates that you take 2 seconds to contract the muscle, and immediately take another two seconds to return to the starting position. A tempo of 2-2-2 indicates that you take 2 seconds to contract the muscle, stop for two seconds, then take two seconds to return to the starting position.

Rest

This is the number of minutes of rest you must take between each set.

THE WORKOUTS

Strength

Increasing your strength will allow you to improve the force you can exert, which has a great influence on the power you can generate. Below is a strength workout. You will want to train at 70 percent of 1RM for each exercise and perform the maximal number of repetitions you can at each training. Be sure to train each leg individually. Photos for each exercise can be found in the Exercises chapter of the book.

Strength Workout					
Exercise	Sets	Reps	Weight	Tempo	Rest
Seated Leg Press Machine	3	Max	70% 1RM	2-0-2	90 sec.
Leg Extension	3	Max	70% 1RM	2-0-2	90 sec.
Machine Leg Curl	3	Max	70% 1RM	2-0-2	90 sec.
Barbell Bench Press	3	Max	70% 1RM	2-0-2	90 sec.
Machine Calf Raise	3	Max	70% 1RM	2-0-2	90 sec.
Machine Leg Curl Feet Pointing	3	Max	70% 1RM	2-0-2	90 sec.
Machine Hip Flexion	3	Max	70% 1RM	2-0-2	90 sec.
Squat On Smith Machine	3	Max	70% 1RM	2-0-2	90 sec.
Machine Calf Raise	3	Max	70% 1RM	2-0-2	90 sec.
Machine Biceps Curl Supination Grip	3	Max	70% 1RM	2-0-2	90 sec.
Machine Triceps Extension	3	Max	70% 1RM	2-0-2	90 sec.
Cable Lat Pull Down Supination Grip	3	Max	70% 1RM	2-0-2	90 sec.
Machine Shoulder Press	3	Max	70% 1RM	2-0-2	90 sec.

Explosive power

Explosive power will be trained using plyometrics. During plyometrics, you need to contract your muscles as fast as you can. You need to proceed with high velocity contraction. Complete a good warm-up before training. You must contract each muscle group as fast as you can for each repetition. Photos for each exercise can be found in the Exercises chapter of the book.

Explosive Power Workout				
Exercise	Sets	Reps	Tempo	Rest
45° Jumps 1 foot To The Other Skating Style	6-8	1	Fast contr	45 sec.
Abductor Dynamic Crossover	6-8	1	Fast contr	45 sec.
Calf Jump	6-8	1	Fast contr	45 sec.
Explosive Push-Ups	6-8	1	Fast contr	45 sec.
Depth Jump	6-8	1	Fast contr	45 sec.
Start Running From The Floor / Acceleration	6-8	1	Fast contr	45 sec.
Hand Clap Push-Ups	6-8	1	Fast contr	45 sec.
Touching foot with opposite hand	6-8	1	Fast contr	45 sec.
Side Jump Skater Style	6-8	1	Fast contr	45 sec.

Power

As explosive power primarily relates to the rate of force you produce in the first milliseconds of the contraction, when I address the notion of power, I am referring to the power you can generate in the first 25 seconds of skating at full capacity.

Below are two power workouts. For the first workout, you will want to train at 50 percent of 1RM for each exercise and perform the maximal number of repetitions you can at each training. For the second workout, you will want to train at 60 percent of 1RM for each exercise. Be sure to train each leg individually in both workouts. Photos for each exercise can be found in the Exercises chapter of the book.

Power Workout 1

Exercise	Sets	Reps	Weight	Tempo	Rest
Seated Leg Press Machine	3	Max	50% 1RM	Fast contr	120 sec.
Leg Extension	3	Max	50% 1RM	Fast contr	120 sec.
Machine Leg Curl	3	Max	50% 1RM	Fast contr	120 sec.
Barbell Bench Press	3	Max	50% 1RM	Fast contr	120 sec.
Machine Calf Raise	3	Max	50% 1RM	Fast contr	120 sec.
Machine Leg Curl Feet Pointing	3	Max	50% 1RM	Fast contr	120 sec.
Machine Hip Flexion	3	Max	50% 1RM	Fast contr	120 sec.
Squat On Smith Machine	3	Max	50% 1RM	Fast contr	120 sec.
Machine Calf Raise	3	Max	50% 1RM	Fast contr	120 sec.
Machine Biceps Curl Supination Grip	3	Max	50% 1RM	Fast contr	120 sec.
Machine Triceps Extension	3	Max	50% 1RM	Fast contr	120 sec.
Cable Lat Pull Down Supination Grip	3	Max	50% 1RM	Fast contr	120 sec.
Machine Shoulder Press	3	Max	50% 1RM	Fast contr	120 sec.

Power Workout 2

Exercise	Sets	Reps	Weight	Tempo	Rest
Seated Leg Press Machine	3	Max	60% 1RM	Fast contr	120 sec.
Leg Extension	3	Max	60% 1RM	Fast contr	120 sec.
Machine Leg Curl	3	Max	60% 1RM	Fast contr	120 sec.
Barbell Bench Press	3	Max	60% 1RM	Fast contr	120 sec.
Machine Calf Raise	3	Max	60% 1RM	Fast contr	120 sec.
Machine Leg Curl Feet Pointing	3	Max	60% 1RM	Fast contr	120 sec.
Machine Hip Flexion	3	Max	60% 1RM	Fast contr	120 sec.
Squat On Smith Machine	3	Max	60% 1RM	Fast contr	120 sec.
Machine Calf Raise	3	Max	60% 1RM	Fast contr	120 sec.
Machine Biceps Curl Supination Grip	3	Max	60% 1RM	Fast contr	120 sec.
Machine Triceps Extension	3	Max	60% 1RM	Fast contr	120 sec.
Cable Lat Pull Down Supination Grip	3	Max	60% 1RM	Fast contr	120 sec.
Machine Shoulder Press	3	Max	60% 1RM	Fast contr	120 sec.

Anaerobic power

Anaerobic power relates to the highest power you can achieve and sustain for a long period of time (above 50 seconds) whithout getting exhausted. Here, you'll use weight training to improve the capacity of your leg muscles to produce high intensity work (under anaerobic conditions). You must also keep in mind that this kind of training involves pain. In most cases, the preferred activity to improve anaerobic power is training on a bike or treadmill doing intervals. While I do agree that intervals are a great way to achieve this, you can also use weight training. However, make sure you don't sacrifice the aerobic aspect of your training.

Below are two anaerobic power workouts. For the first workout, you will want to train at 30 percent of 1RM for each exercise and perform the maximal number of repetitions you can at each training. For the second workout, you will want to train at 40 percent of 1RM for each exercise. Be sure to train each leg individually in both workouts, except for Seated Leg Press Machine and Squat on Smith Machine. Photos for each exercise can be found in the Exercises chapter of the book.

Anaerobic Power Workout 1					
Exercise	Sets	Reps	Weight	Tempo	Rest
Seated Leg Press Machine	3	Max	30% 1RM	Fast contr	120 sec.
Leg Extension	3	Max	30% 1RM	Fast contr	120 sec.
Machine Leg Curl	3	Max	30% 1RM	Fast contr	120 sec.
Machine Hip Flexion	3	Max	30% 1RM	Fast contr	120 sec.
Squat On Smith Machine	3	Max	30% 1RM	Fast contr	120 sec.
Machine Calf Raise	3	Max	30% 1RM	Fast contr	120 sec.

Anaerobic Power Workout 2					
Exercise	Sets	Reps	Weight	Tempo	Rest
Seated Leg Press Machine	3	Max	40% 1RM	Fast contr	120 sec.
Leg Extension	3	Max	40% 1RM	Fast contr	120 sec.
Machine Leg Curl	3	Max	40% 1RM	Fast contr	120 sec.
Machine Hip Flexion	3	Max	40% 1RM	Fast contr	120 sec.
Squat On Smith Machine	3	Max	40% 1RM	Fast contr	120 sec.
Machine Calf Raise	3	Max	40% 1RM	Fast contr	120 sec.

Upper body

As you may have guessed, your upper body needs a different kind of training. Yes, you need strength and explosive power (for shooting the puck), but developing your hand skills is of utmost importance. However, this workout will only address the development of lower body strength and explosive power. Developing hands skills could be the subject of a whole other book. Be sure to train each leg individually. Photos for each exercise can be found in the Exercises chapter of the book.

Upper Body Workout					
Exercise	Sets	Reps	Weight	Tempo	Rest
Barbell Close grip Bench Press	3	Max	70% 1RM	2-0-2	90 sec
Barbell Bench Press	3	Max	70% 1RM	2-0-2	90 sec
Machine Biceps Curl Supination Grip	3	Max	70% 1RM	2-0-2	90 sec
Machine Triceps Extension	3	Max	70% 1RM	2-0-2	90 sec
Cable Lat Pull Down Supination Grip	3	Max	70% 1RM	2-0-2	90 sec
Powell Raise	2	10-12		2-0-2	60 sec
Dumbbell External Rotator On Swiss Ball	2	10-12		2-0-2	60 sec
Neck Strengthening On Swiss Ball - Front	2	10-12		2-0-2	60 sec
Neck Strengthening On Swiss Ball - Side	2	10-12		2-0-2	60 sec
Hand Work / Squeeze Ball	2	10-12		2-0-2	60 sec
Fingers Work With Elastic	2	10-12		2-0-2	60 sec
Dumbbell Wrist Flexion On Swiss Ball	2	10-12		2-0-2	60 sec

Abs and low back workout

Your abs and low back musculature plays, as in many other sports, an important role in performance. So it's necessary to take time to build and maintain the efficiency of these muscle groups.

Abs and Low Back Workout				
Exercise	**Sets**	**Reps**	**Tempo**	**Rest**
Abdominals / Crunch	1	8-12	2-2-2	60 sec
Swiss Ball Abdominal Crunch With Dumbbell	1	8-12	2-2-2	60 sec
Abdominal Trunk and Leg Raise	1	8-12	2-2-2	60 sec
Abdominal Oblique	1	8-12	2-2-2	60 sec
Abdominal Oblique Hang Hip Twist	1	8-12	2-2-2	60 sec
Abdominal Oblique / Shoulders	1	45 sec		60 sec
Leg Raise	1	8-12	2-2-2	60 sec
Back Extension On Swiss Ball	1	8-12	2-2-2	60 sec
Front Plank On Swiss Ball	1	45 sec		60 sec
Side Plank Running Style / Oblique - Abductor	1	45 sec		60 sec

Recovery

Stimulation, and not stress, is the key element to consider if you want to reach the best fitness level possible. So, stress means too much training and not enough recovery periods. The recovery workout will allow you to stay active, but the lower intensity of the workout is there to make sure your muscles will have time to build the energetic reserves they need and adapt to the training they must sustain. Even if it's indicated that you must do a maximal number of repetitions at 50 percent of 1 RM, stop when you begin to feel muscle fatigue. Remember that recovery must be a part of your training. Be sure to train each leg individually.

Recovery Workout					
Exercise	Sets	Reps	Weight	Tempo	Rest
Seated Leg Press Machine	2	8-10	50% 1RM	2-0-2	60 sec
Leg Extension	2	8-10	50% 1RM	2-0-2	60 sec
Machine Leg Curl	2	8-10	50% 1RM	2-0-2	60 sec
Barbell Bench Press	2	8-10	50% 1RM	2-0-2	60 sec
Machine Calf Raise	2	8-10	50% 1RM	2-0-2	60 sec
Machine Leg Curl Feet Pointing	2	8-10	50% 1RM	2-0-2	60 sec
Machine Hip Flexion	2	8-10	50% 1RM	2-0-2	60 sec
Squat On Smith Machine	2	8-10	50% 1RM	2-0-2	60 sec
Machine Calf Raise	2	8-10	50% 1RM	2-0-2	60 sec
Machine Biceps Curl Supination Grip	2	8-10	50% 1RM	2-0-2	60 sec
Machine Triceps Extension	2	8-10	50% 1RM	2-0-2	60 sec
Cable Lat Pull Down Supination Grip	2	8-10	50% 1RM	2-0-2	60 sec
Machine Shoulder Press	2	8-10	50% 1RM	2-0-2	60 sec

On-ice workouts

Here are specific workouts I recommend to improve specific muscular qualities on the ice.

Improving max power

Go with 7 to 9 short-interval skating periods of 15 to 20 seconds at full speed. Take a 2- to 3-minute rest period between each interval. The long rest period allows your muscles to replenish their energy supply. Training on empty muscle reserves, even though you feel like you are training intensely, only guarantees exhaustion rather than adaptation. At all times, training adaptation is what you should strive for.

Improving anaerobic power

Alternately, do between 7 to 9 short skating intervals of 25 to 50 seconds (end your interval when your speed drops significantly). Take a 2- to 3-minute rest period between each interval and 5 to 7 long interval skating periods of 60 to 90 seconds at a speed corresponding to 80 – 90 percent of your maximal speed. Take a 3-minute rest period between each interval.

Improving explosive power

Do 7 to 9 high-speed intervals, skating from one goal line to the other. Make sure you **power-out** from the goal line. Take a 2-minute rest period between each interval.

The training programs

As presented in the training calendar (Table 15), I suggest you do your weight-training program 4 times a week (on Days 1, 2, 5 and 6). Here's the progression you should follow:

Week 1

Day 1	Day 2	Day 5	Day 6
Strength workout	Strength workout + Abs and low back workout	Power workout 1	Power workout 2

Week 2

Day 1	Day 2	Day 5	Day 6
Strength workout + Abs and low back workout	Power workout 1	Strength and upper body workout	Explosive power workout

Week 3

Day 1	Day 2	Day 5	Day 6
Strength workout + Abs and low back workout	Power workout 1	On-ice workout: Improving max power	Explosive power workout

Week 4

Day 1	Day 2	Day 5	Day 6
Anaerobic power workout 1 + Abs and low back workout	Explosive power workout	Strength and upper body workout + On-ice workout: Improving max power	Anaerobic power workout 2

Week 6

Day 1	Day 2	Day 5	Day 6
Strength workout + Abs and low back workout	On-ice workout: Improving anaerobic power + Anaerobic power workout 1	Power workout 2	Anaerobic power workout 2 + Abs and low back workout

Week 7

Day 1	Day 2	Day 5	Day 6
Power workout 1	Explosive power workout	Anaerobic power workout 1 + Abs and low back workout	On-ice workout: Improving explosive power

Week 8

Day 1	Day 2	Day 5	Day 6
Recovery workout	Recovery workout	Recovery workout	Recovery workout

Week 9

In order to evaluate your progression and adjust your program to your improved fitness level, I invite you to repeat the Strength testing protrocol and the Speed-Strength testing protocol.

Day 1	Day 2	Day 5	Day 6
Strength testing protocol	Recovery workout	Speed-Strength testing protocol	Anaerobic power workout 1 + Abs and low back workout

Week 10

Day 1	Day 2	Day 5	Day 6
Strength and upper body workout	Anaerobic power workout 2 + Abs and low back workout	Power workout 2 + Abs and low back workout	On-ice workout: improving explosive power

Week 11

Day 1	Day 2	Day 5	Day 6
Explosive power workout	Anaerobic power workout 1 + Abs and low back workout	Power workout 1	Anaerobic power workout 2

Week 12

Day 1	Day 2	Day 5	Day 6
Explosive power workout + Abs and low back workout	Strength workout and upper body workout + On-ice workout: improving anaerobic power	Anaerobic power workout 2	Anaerobic power workout 2 + Abs and low back workout

Week 13

Day 1	Day 2	Day 5	Day 6
Power workout 2	Power workout 1 + On-ice workout: improving explosive power	Anaerobic power workout 1 + Abs and low back workout	Anaerobic power workout 2

Week 14

Day 1	Day 2	Day 5	Day 6
Strength workout + Abs and low back workout	Anaerobic power workout 2 + On-ice workout: improving max power	Power workout 1	Explosive power workout

Week 15

Day 1	Day 2	Day 3	Day 4
Explosive power workout	Anaerobic power workout 1	Anaerobic power workout 2 + Abs and low back workout	Power workout 2

Week 16

Day 1	Day 2	Day 5	Day 6
Anaerobic power workout 1 + Abs and low back workout	Power workout 1	Strength and upper body workout + Abs and low back workout	Strength workout

CHAPTER 7
EXERCISES

CORE

Abdominal Oblique / Standing

Abdominal Oblique / Back

Abdominal Oblique / Shoulders - Keep the abs tight and your body straight. Stand on one foot. Make circle with the ball on the floor keeping your arms straight.

Dr. Denis Boucher, Ph.D.

Abdominal Oblique Hang Hip Twist - Keep abs tight. Keep knees high.

Abdominal Oblique with Swiss Ball - Keep the abs tight and back flat on the floor (to start). Roll the ball on the side of your thighs. Alternate.

Dr. Denis Boucher, Ph.D.

Abdominal Trunk and Leg Raise - Keep your back flat on the bench at the beginning and abs tight. Keep your legs straight and lift them up with your body.

Abdominals / Crunch

Dr. Denis Boucher, Ph.D.

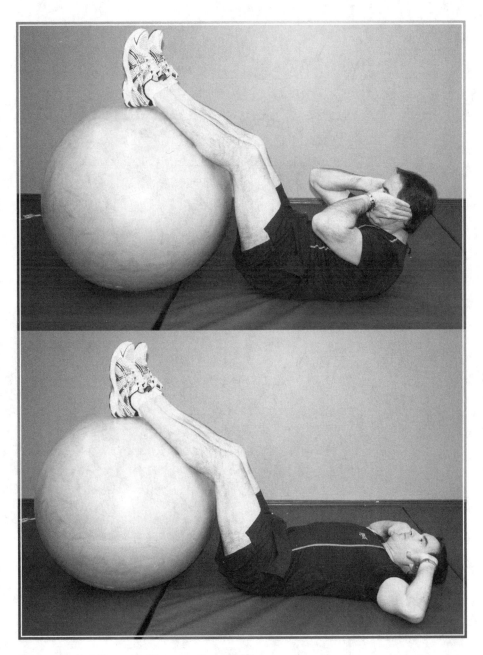

Abdominals / Crunch (Feet on Swissball)

Abdominals / Crunch (Swissball on Knees) - Keep the abdominal tight and back flat on the floor (to start). Push the ball up. Push in the ball (more advanced).

Dr. Denis Boucher, Ph.D.

Back Extension On Swiss Ball

Front Plank On Swiss Ball - Keep back and legs straight and your abs tight. Place your feet on the ball. Keep position.

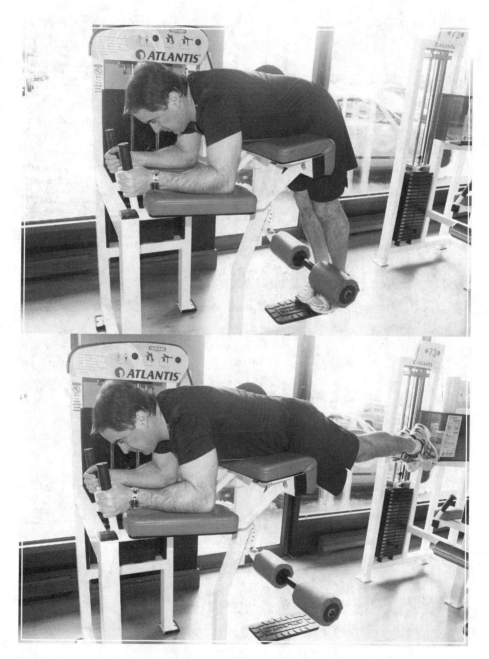

Leg Raise - Keep back straight and abs tight Raise legs aligned with body.

Side Plank Running Style / Oblique – Abductor - Keep abs tight. Running movement.

Dr. Denis Boucher, Ph.D.

Swiss Ball Abdominal Crunch With Dumbbell - Keep your abs tight and your arms perpendicular to the ground. Hold a stability ball behind your knees. Raise the body up while holding weights in your hands. Pronation grip.

STRETCHING/FLEXIBILITY

Adductors Machine

Dr. Denis Boucher, Ph.D.

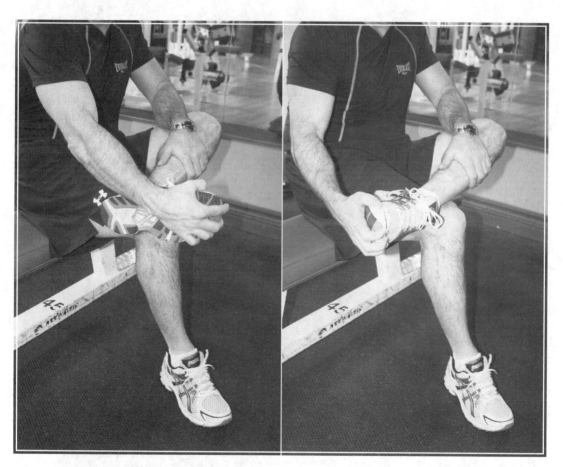

Ankle Range Of Motion

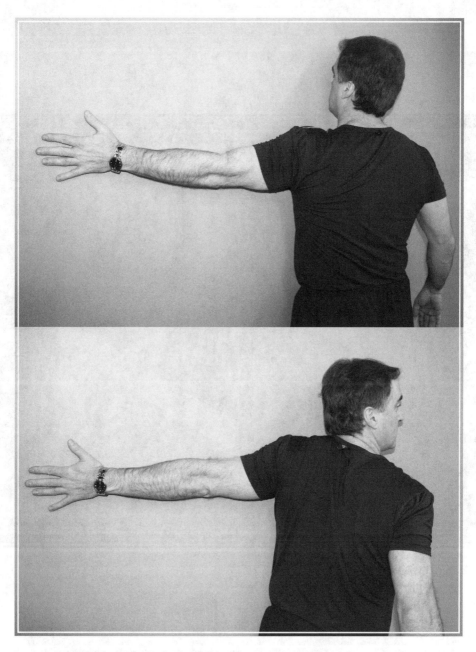

Anterior Shoulder Pectoral Flexibility

Back / Hamstrings Stretch

Back Buttocks And Thigh Stretching

Dr. Denis Boucher, Ph.D.

Back Buttocks Flexibility

Back Flexibility

Dr. Denis Boucher, Ph.D.

Back Flexibility / Trunk Rotation

Back Leg Flexibility

Dr. Denis Boucher, Ph.D.

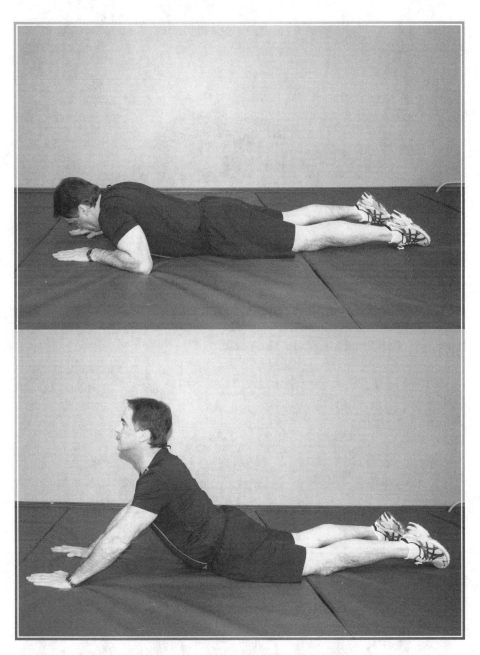

Back Stretching

Back Swiss Ball Stretching - On The Back

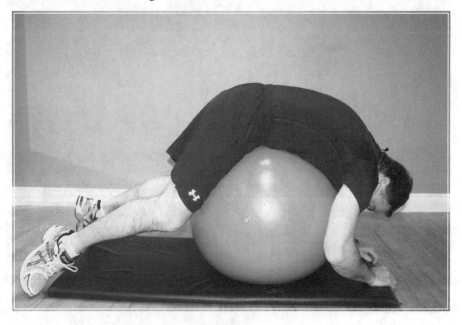

Back Swiss Ball Stretching - On The Belly

Dr. Denis Boucher, Ph.D.

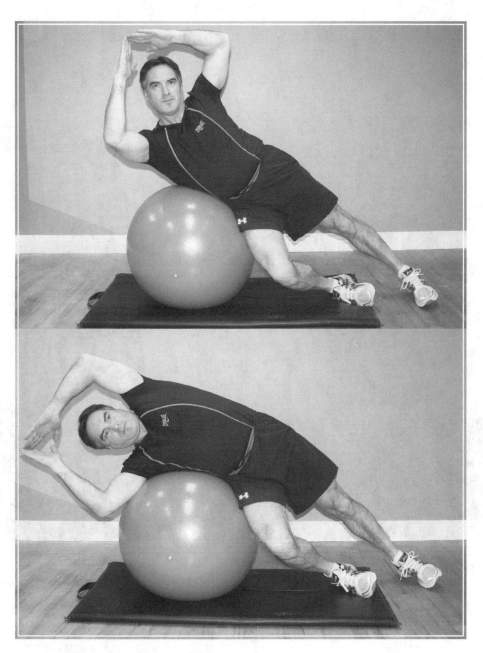

Back Swiss Ball Stretching - On The Side

Back Trunk Stretching

Dr. Denis Boucher, Ph.D.

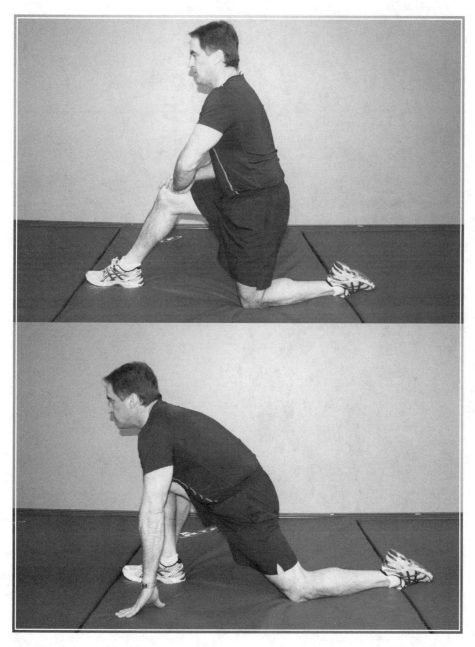

Calf / Buttocks Flexibility

Dumbbell External Rotator On Swiss Ball

Dr. Denis Boucher, Ph.D.

Leg Gluteal Stretch

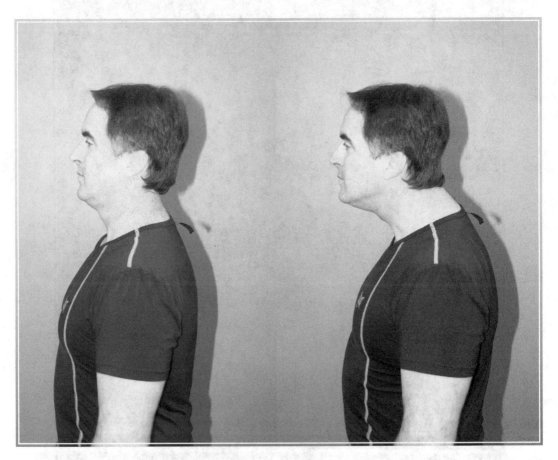

Neck Range Of Motion - On The Front

Dr. Denis Boucher, Ph.D.

Neck Range Of Motion - On The Side

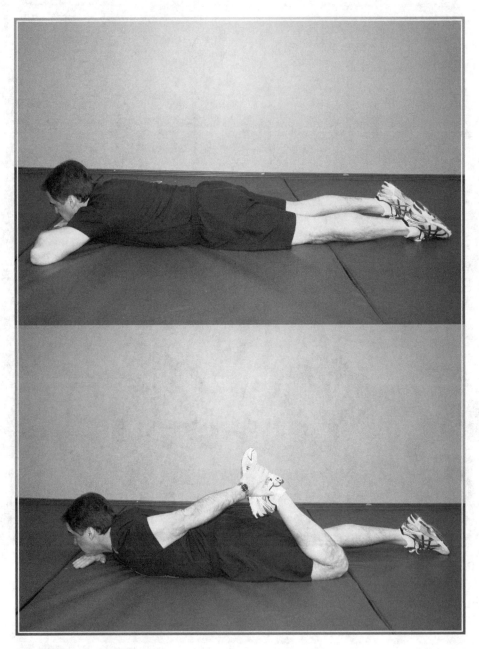

Quadriceps Stretching

Dr. Denis Boucher, Ph.D.

Seated Forward Flexion

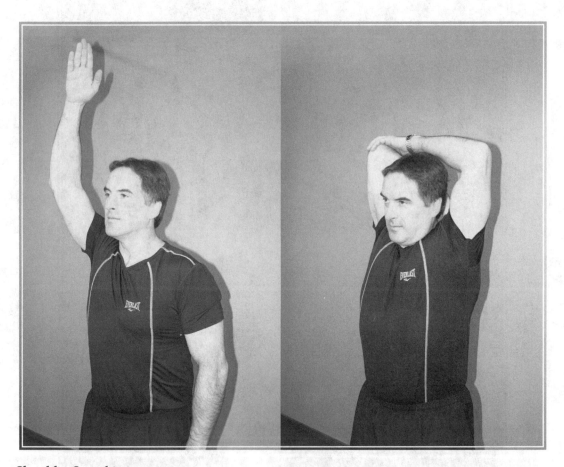

Shoulder Stretching

Swiss Ball Flexibility Leg

Thigh And Back Stretching

Dr. Denis Boucher, Ph.D.

Touching foot with opposite hand

ARMS/FOREARMS

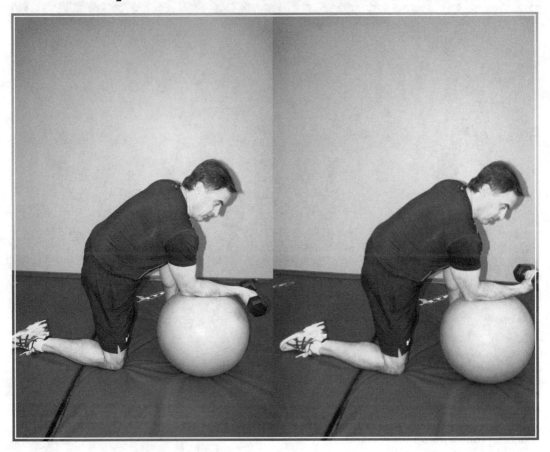

Dumbbell Wrist Flexion On Swiss Ball

Dr. Denis Boucher, Ph.D.

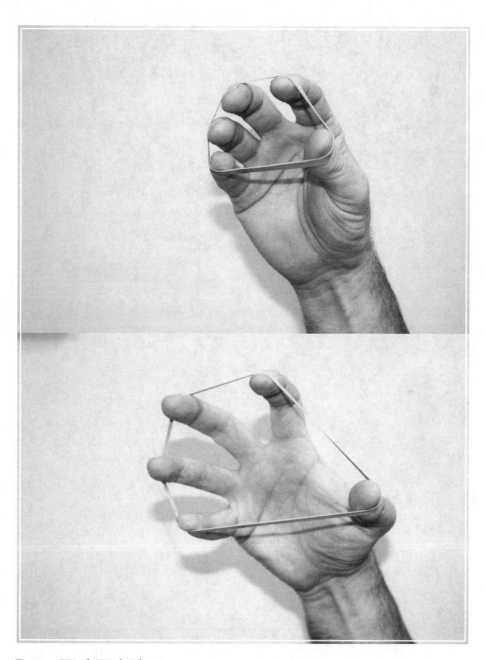

Fingers Work With Elastic

Hand Work / Squeeze Ball

Dr. Denis Boucher, Ph.D.

Machine Biceps Curl Supination Grip - Keep back straight, abs tight.

Machine Triceps Extension - Keep your back straight and elbows supported. Neutral or hammer grip.

CHEST

Barbell Bench Press

Explosive Push-Ups

Dr. Denis Boucher, Ph.D.

Hand Clap Push-Ups

Start Running From The Floor / Acceleration

Dr. Denis Boucher, Ph.D.

LATS

Cable Lat Pull Down Supination Grip - Keep back straight and abs tight. Pull with your arms aligned with cable. Supination grip.

LEGS

45° Jumps 1 foot To The Other Skating Style

Dr. Denis Boucher, Ph.D.

Abductor Dynamic Crossover

Calf Jump

Dr. Denis Boucher, Ph.D.

Depth Jump

Leg Extension (One Leg) - Keep your back straight and abs tight. Raise one leg completely extended. Alternate

Dr. Denis Boucher, Ph.D.

Leg Extension (Two Legs) - Keep your back straight and abs tight.

Machine Calf Raise - Keep back straight, leg straight and head over foot Ball of the foot on the step.

Dr. Denis Boucher, Ph.D.

Machine Calf Raise (Smith Machine, One Leg) - Keep back straight, leg straight and head over foot Ball of the foot on the step.

Machine Calf Raise (Smith Machine, Two Legs) - Keep back straight, leg straight and head over foot Ball of the foot on the step.

Machine Hip Flexion - Keep your abs tight, back straight and head up. Pull the knee up to hip (or higher).

Machine Leg Curl - - Keep the abs tight and your stomach on the bench. Pull both legs at the same time.

Dr. Denis Boucher, Ph.D.

Machine Leg Curl Feet Pointing - Keep the feet pointing.

Seated Leg Press Machine

Side Jump Skater Style

Squat On Smith Machine - Keep back straight. Head up. Chest out.

NECK

Neck Strengthening On Swiss Ball – Front

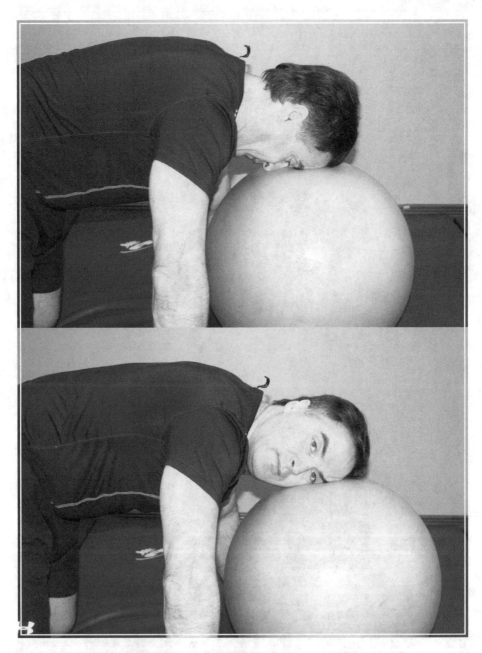

Neck Strengthening On Swiss Ball – Side

Dr. Denis Boucher, Ph.D.

SHOULDERS

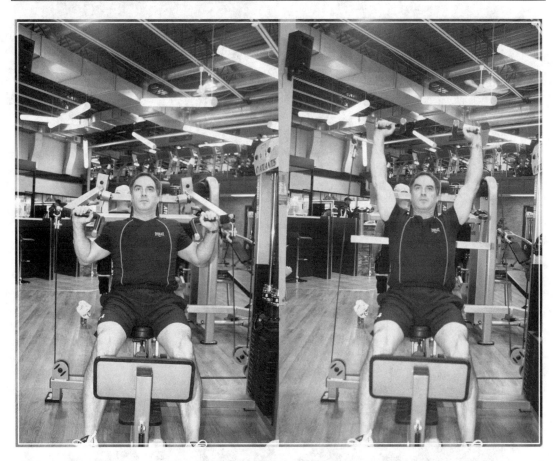

Machine Shoulder Press - Keep the back straight, abs tight and head up. Elbows forward, push up, keeping elbows under the bar.

Powell Raise

Dr. Denis Boucher, Ph.D.

CHAPTER 8
HOW TO BECOME A GREAT HOCKEY PLAYER

As I mentioned above, being physically fit makes you a great athlete, but it doesn't necessarily make you a great hockey player. To achieve greatness in this sport, you need to be disciplined and, in my opinion, consider hockey as a sport that requires a total investment of your mind and body.

To better understand what I'm talking about, here's an interview that Jàn Bortàk, a Slovak hockey journalist writing for Czech Web site www.nhlpro.cz who specializes in the National Hockey League, conducted with me. I think his questions were very relevant, and I hope my answers will be useful to you:

Q: In your recent article in *The Hockey News*, you advise the players to train their brain, because it helps their performance. Do you mean that players in the NHL are aware of how important their brain is and think about their play, or do they still focus especially on their physical preparation?

A: *I think that many players are well aware of the importance of their mental capacities on performance. However, since there is no standardized approach in this area, many of them ignore this aspect of training.*

So far, it's hard to make a direct correlation between mental training and performance. Athletes know it's important, but they don't really know what "brain qualities" to train and how these qualities influence performance. It's not as clear as physical training: the better your fitness level, the more likely you are to perform…

Furthermore, we can measure fitness progress following training, and we have a pretty good idea of what "amount" of training you need to improve aerobic and muscular qualities, but what amount of training do you need to improve attention? So far, nobody can answer this question.

Also, what is mental preparation? This is a tough question to answer. Mine is quite simple: make sure the athlete "perceives" he has the capacities to accomplish his task. The answer is simple, but accomplishing this turns out to be a major challenge. Thus, the athlete must "perceive" he can achieve his goals, he must feel he has the resources he needs to achieve them and, finally, he must use the right strategies. As you can understand, mental preparation involves a lot of "mental work". This work varies from one athlete to the other, from one game to the other. Scientists have guidelines for mental preparation, but they always have to be adapted.

Q: What do you think about giving the resolutions before the season? For example, if some defenseman sets a goal to get to the nominees on the Norris Trophy. Is there not (except for motivation) a risk of too strong pressure, which can lead to unsatisfactory performance? According to you, which kinds of goals should players set before the season?

A: *Goals must be realistic and manageable. As I mentioned earlier, this means that the player must "perceive" he can achieve the goal, he must feel he has the capacities to achieve it and he must use the correct strategies to progress towards it. If one of these elements is missing, the athlete will perceive an increasing gap between what he thinks he can accomplish and the goal he has to achieve. At this point, the goal becomes a point of stress that hinders his performance, as opposed to a motivating force.*

In sports, nothing should merely remain a mental thought. A mental thought must lead to specific behaviors that bring the athlete closer to his goal. Then, the athlete will feel confident and improve his performance.

Q: Which mental elements (self-confidence, positive thinking, satisfaction with oneself, other…) are important in addition to summer physical training (fitness, strength, endurance) for players to have a successful season?

A: *I think self-confidence is a major element. In every aspect of life, your brain rules… Even if everything shows that you're one of the best in your field, if you don't believe in your abilities, reality won't help you; your brain will automatically focus on every little detail that will "reinforce" your belief that you're not good enough.*

Believing you have the capacities to reach your goals is really important. But for this self-confidence to remain stable over time, you must always try to reach realistic and manageable goals.

Now, you may ask, "what is a realistic and manageable goal"? Well, it's a goal that creates a gap between your current and desired performance level. What makes it realistic and manageable, however, is that you "perceive" that you are able to close this gap. More importantly, the goal is so clearly defined that it allows you to plan the training you need to progress towards it.

If the goal is not realistic and manageable, you will face uncertainty because what you're trying to achieve is too vague. You won't know what to do to achieve it. You will feel a constantly increasing gap between where you are and where you should be. You will lose your self-confidence. And, eventually, your performance will decrease without anybody ever knowing why. It's the worst-case scenario.

Q: What is the line between positive thinking and satisfaction with oneself? Is not there a risk that the player's satisfaction with his performance may lead to stagnation or deterioration of his previous performances?

A: *When you've reached the point where you think you have achieved every goal you've set in your career, there is no more "gap" to eliminate. The result is stagnation. In order to progress, an athlete must always think about the game and ways to improve his performance. To accomplish this, he needs to set new realistic and manageable goals that will create a gap that he will want to close. Without this, no improvement is possible.*

DR. DENIS BOUCHER, PH.D.

Q: If a player fails and coach lets him sit in the stands during several matches and his ice time is reduced, how should this player avoid disappointment, disenchantment or depression? What should he do (psychologically) in order to endure tough times and manage to get his lost position in the team?

A: *There are three ways an athlete can manage pressure and disappointment: deny the problem, repress his emotions or deal with the problem directly. Denying the existence of the problem and repressing emotions are counterproductive. Facing the problem, thinking about solutions and showing you want to improve yourself is the only way you can get back on track. However, to succeed with this process, the athlete must set aside his own ego… Definitely one of the hardest things to do.*

Q: After winning the Stanley Cup, players often lose their motivation for some time and their performances in the next season usually go down (such as Chicago, Carolina or Anaheim after lock out). How should they motivate during the short summer and celebrate the victory before the next season to be at least as good as they were in previous season?

A: *Life is a cycle. A hockey season is a cycle. Pressure, pleasure, emotions, the desire to win, etc. all have their own cycle throughout the season. Progressing towards the Stanley Cup involves a build-up of tension and emotions that have to fade away after the Stanley Cup has been won. It's normal that in the summer no player has the same desire to win the Stanley Cup. Everyone must accept that. Then, if at the beginning of the season you ask for the same intensity level you had before winning the Stanley Cup, you are actually making a big mistake, because this is not a realistic and manageable goal. It's something that is impossible to reach at this point in the life cycle of the hockey season. You must understand the existence of this cycle and build motivation around it throughout the season. Motivation has its own cycle. A player having fun may appear to have a low level of motivation but perform well. If you ask him to change his attitude, you may affect him in the wrong way. Measure the performance level of the player first before you assume he's not motivated. Motivation is often very poorly understood.*

Q: Rookies after tremendous first season in NHL are often less successful in next season. Ok, opponents give them more attention and they are under greater pressure, but which are other (especially mental) reasons for their weaker performance?

A: *I would say there is likely a different reason for each player… But in my opinion, loss of focus is a killer. You're a young man who dreamt about making the NHL. One day you're there. It's your first season; you're giving all you can to prove you belong there. Then something happens, fame, money… you have it all. Your brain is now flooded with many new and interesting things that you deserve after all those years of sacrifice. Your attention is captured elsewhere. If too much attention is shifted away from the game… you're doomed to fail.*

Also, I've prepared a short document for a team entitled *How to Become a Great Hockey Player.* As you will see, physical training is only one part of what you need to become a great hockey player. This document is presented below with no further explanation. It also summarizes most of the topics covered so far. I'm including this to make sure you'll always be aware that you need to be in control of yourself to succeed.

HOW TO BECOME A GREAT HOCKEY PLAYER (GUIDELINES)

1. How to train strategically

Rule 1: Evaluate your current fitness level

- Strength
- Power
- Speed
- Aerobic and anaerobic capacity
- Biomechanic efficiency (skating technique)

Rule 2: Know what you need to achieve

- Strength
- Power
- Speed
- Aerobic and anaerobic capacity
- Biomechanic efficiency (skating technique)

You must be able to define the gap between your current fitness level and what you need to achieve.

Rule 3: Determine measurable fitness goals

- Increase lower body strength: 12%
- Increase skating power: 20 watts
- Increase speed: 1km/h in the first 10 seconds
- Aerobic and anaerobic capacity: increase maximal lactate steady state to 45%
- Biomechanic efficiency (skating technique): increase duration of the push-off phase.

Rule 4: Follow a training program specific to your needs (your goals).

Rule 5: Prevent overtraining and plan for recovery periods.

Rule 6: Know when you've achieved your fitness goals.

- **You won't always need to improve your fitness level. Someday you'll reach the best fitness level for you.**

2. Stress management

The stress that you experience is essentially influenced by several aspects which include:

- perception of the situation: how you see the situation, which may be different from what it actually is;
- perception of the available resources and whether you believe they're adequate to face the situation. Your perception of the current availability of resources, and your assessment of whether these resources are adequate, may or may not be realistic;
- perception of the influence that you have over a particular situation;
- your mental and emotional control abilities;
- your perception of your ability to undertake certain tasks and functions;
- past experiences (be it success or failure) regarding the situation;
- your perception of the root of the problem.

Stress and goal-setting

As stress is proportional to the difference between your current capabilities and your goals, the smaller this difference is, the lower the stress.

Ways to manage stress

- Deny the problem (worst possible strategy).
- Deal with your negative emotions (energy-consuming strategy without positive results in most cases).
- Thinking of the best strategy to address the problem (the most effective approach).

Finding the best stress level

- You can't feel "nothing" (unless you'r dead).
- You can feel "too much" (negative stress).
- You can be in the middle, feeling the challenge you know you can face.

How to manage stress

- Step 1: Write down your fears and negative emotions.
- Step 2: Allow your fears and emotions to exist (never try not to think about them).
- Step 3: Don't believe the worst-case scenarios your brain creates (observe from a distance).
- Step 4: Write down the strategies that will allow you to go ahead and solve the problem or improve the situation.
- Step 5: Test the strategies in order to find and use the best ones.

Dr. Denis Boucher, Ph.D.

3. Mental preparation (before each game)

Step 1: Rehearse the game plan.
Step 2: Know your role and accept it.
Step 3: Decide to play as a team.
Step 4: Manage your stress.
Step 5: Think of your skills.
Step 6: Focus on the challenge you are facing.
Step 7: Remember the actions you must take on the ice.

This entire thought process will lead you to adopt the behaviors that result in success.

4. Concentration

It's about bringing your mind back to the goals you need to achieve, the skills you have, the strategies to follow and the behaviors to adopt.

Concentration leads to action.

5. Motivation

The natural result of a clear focus on what you need to accomplish and how to accomplish it.

You lose motivation when your mind focuses on vague goals that nobody (even you) knows how to achieve.

Realistic and manageable goals lead to the adoption of specific behaviors that bring results. Results bring improvement. Improvement leads to success. Success = Motivation.

6.   Team-building

How a player perceives his teammates and how his teammates perceive him determine team cohesion.

If you want team cohesion, leaving behind your judgments and impressions is of utmost importance, because every player will try to achieve the goal with his own knowledge and personality.

If you judge a player on his personality, you will destroy team cohesion.

If you want team cohesion, don't judge a player on his personality, judge him on the results.

Why ask a player to change his personality if he has good results? No reason at all.

CONCLUSION

If you want to become a great athlete, you need to train strategically. Without a great fitness level (on the ice), you can't become a great hockey player. Sadly, a high fitness level can't guarantee you'll become a great hockey player. To achieve this, there are many other factors you need to consider and aspects to train for.

To become a great hockey player, you need to master many physical and mental qualities that are completely different from other athletic activities, which is what makes hockey such a distinctive sport.

I hope this book will help you pave your way to success.

DR. DENIS BOUCHER, PH.D.

REFERENCES

1. Bundle, M. W. & Weyand, P. G. Sprint Exercise Performance. *Exercise and Sport Sciences Reviews* 40, 174–182 (2012).

2. Poole, D. C., Barstow, T. J., Mcdonough, P. & Jones, A. M. Control of Oxygen Uptake during Exercise. *Medicine & Science in Sports & Exercise* 40, 462–474 (2008).

3. Boucher, D. Player fitness in the playoffs. *The Hockey News* (2012).at <http://www.thehockeynews.com/articles/47429-Player-fitness-in-the-playoffs.html>

4. Boucher, D. The development of on-ice testing. (2010).at <http://www.thehockeynews.com/articles/35534-Denis-Bouchers-Blog-The-development-of-onice-testing.html>

5. Boucher, D. On-ice testing with the Philadelphia Flyers. *The Hockey News* (2012).at <http://www.thehockeynews.com/articles/44301-On-ice-testing-with-the-Philadelphia-Flyers.html>

6. Brooks, G. A., Fahey, T. D. & Baldwin, K. M. Metabolic Response to Exercise. *Exercise Physiology: Human Bioenergetics and Its Application* 213–240 (2005).

7. Harris, J. A. & Benedict, F. G. *A biometric study of basal metabolism in man.* (Washington Carnegie Institution of Washington: 1919).at <http://archive.org/details/biometricstudyof00harruoft>

8. Kenttä, G. & Hassmén, P. Overtraining and Recovery : A conceptual Model. 26, 1–16 (1998).

9. Raglin, J. S. Overtraining and staleness: psychometric monitoring of endurance athletes. *Handbook of research on sport psychology* (1993).

10. O'Conner, P. J. Overtraining and staleness. *Physical activity and mental health* 145–160 (1998).

11. Gross, J. D. Hardiness and mood disturbances in swimmers while overtraining. *Journal of Sport and Exercise Psychology* 16, 135–149

12. Reid, K. F. & Fielding, R. A. Skeletal Muscle Power: A Critical Determinant of Physical Functioning in Older Adults. *Exercise and Sport Sciences Reviews* 40, 4–12 (2012).

13. Tillin, N. A., Jimenez-Reyes, P., Pain, M. T. G. & Folland, J. P. Neuromuscular Performance of Explosive Power Athletes versus Untrained Individuals. *Medicine & Science in Sports & Exercise* 42, 781–790 (2010).

14. Koning, D., J, J., Houdijk, H., de Groot, G. & Bobbert, M. F. From biomechanical theory to application in top sports: the Klapskate story. *Journal of Biomechanics* 33, 1225–1229 (2000).
15. Shen, W., St-Onge, M.-P., Wang, Z. & Heymsfield, S. B. Study of Body Composition: An Overview. *Human Body Composition*
16. Burnley, M., Davison, G. & Baker, J. R. Effects of Priming Exercise on V˙O2 Kinetics and the Power-Duration Relationship. *Medicine & Science in Sports & Exercise* 43, 2171–2179 (2011).

BIOGRAPHY

Dr. Denis Boucher holds a Ph.D. degree in experimental medicine and a Master's degree in exercise science. He owns an exercise physiology laboratory where he provides services related to sport performance, nutrition, weight management and metabolic analysis.

Dr. Boucher has been involved with the Philadephia Flyers since 1999, conducting the pre-season on-ice fitness evaluation of the players. He authors a blog for the *The Hockey News* magazine and is also co-founder of M2M Lab Inc., a company specialized in the field of real-time physiological monitoring and human factor research. Dr. Boucher is currently producing and hosting video training programs related to sport performance, nutrition and weight loss.

Contact information:

Dr. Denis Boucher, Ph.D.
www.denisboucher.com
info@denisboucher.com
1-866-697-0537 ext. 201

INDEX

DR. DENIS BOUCHER, PH.D.